HILL BIRDS OF SCOTLAND

MALE GOLDEN EAGLE—AFTER THE FIRST FLIGHT FROM THE EYRIE.

HILL BIRDS OF SCOTLAND

BY

SETON GORDON, F.Z.S., M.B.O.U.

AUTHOR OF "THE CHARM OF THE HILLS" AND "BIRDS OF THE
LOCH AND MOUNTAIN"

ILLUSTRATED

LONDON
EDWARD ARNOLD & Co.

First Published October 1915

Reprinted   *October* 1930

Printed in Great Britain by Lowe & Brydone (Printers) Ltd., London.

TO

AUDREY

PREFACE

IT must ever be the case that those birds living their quiet lives on the remote and inaccessible hillsides take from their surroundings a certain charm and distinction.

It is this charm which renders the studying of these mountain dwellers a pursuit of exceptional interest. Many difficulties are set in the way: the hills do not yield the store of their knowledge easily; it is only to him who knows them in storm as in fine weather, and in the dead of winter as well as during long days of June sunlight, that they give a measure of their wisdom. The difficulty of investigating bird life on the highest hills is largely due to the absence of any suitable base in their vicinity; thus I would strongly advise any ornithologist who decides on studying the habits of hill birds to procure a good strong tent, which at the same time is not too heavy to be carried to the high corries.

At elevations of between three and four thousand feet the main inconvenience to the camper is the low temperatures which are experienced after sunset, and a plentiful supply of rugs are a necessity if a night's rest is sought for.

During the months of June and July brilliant weather frequently prevails on the high tops, and even at midnight the afterglow in the north is sufficiently strong to render impossible the changing of photographic plates unless the operator first covers himself with rugs.

These days of early summer, spent at the homes of the Snow Bunting and the Ptarmigan, are retained in the mind's eye for long.

The mists curling smoke-like in the deep glens before the hour of sunrise, the distant hills, heavily snow-flecked, standing sharply against the horizon, the croaking of the Ptarmigan and the flute-like song of the Snow Bunting, all these things are among the priceless memories given by the Spirit of the Great Hills.

SETON GORDON.

CONTENTS

ILLUSTRATIONS

HILL BIRDS OF SCOTLAND

THE GOLDEN EAGLE

IOLAIRE DHUBH, IOLAIRE BHUIDHA (*Gaelic*); ACQUILA CHRYSAETUS (Linn.);
AIGLE ROYAL (*French*); STEINADLER (*German*).

> " Twice the life of a horse, once the life of a man,
> Twice the life of a man, once the life of a stag,
> Twice the life of a stag, once the life of an eagle."

IN the eagle more than in any bird would appear to be
instilled a certain grandeur and nobility of character
which has caused it to be known to many nations as the
King of Birds. The highland chief still wears in his
bonnet three flight feathers of the eagle as a sign of
his chieftainship, and the tail feathers of this royal bird
bedeck the Indian when dressed for battle. To the highlander the eagle has ever been the synonym for great
strength. To him the bird is known as Iolaire dhubh,
or the Black Eagle, and I cannot but think that this title
suits it better than that by which it is known to the Eng-
lish-speaking race. And not among hillmen alone is the
eagle thus spoken of. To the Arab the bird is " Hogarb
kakala," or Black Eagle ; while in Eastern Turkestan,
where it is trained for Falconry, it is called " Karakush,"
or Black Bird. In Spain too the eagle is " Aquila negra,"
though it is also known as Aquila real. Sometimes, on the
west coast of Scotland the eagle receives another name,
and here, perchance, an old shepherd or stalker may
speak of it as " An t'Eun Mōr," or The Great Bird.

A

The eagle has often seemed to me to be in a singularly fortunate position. In the first place, it is without a single formidable enemy, if man be excepted; and then again it is to a great extent independent of the weather for its food supply, for under the most rigorous conditions of continued frost and snow it can still follow its hereditary prey, the unobtrusive ptarmigan and the more demonstrative Red Grouse, as they seek out sheltered quarters till the passing of the storm. I think I am right in saying that the eagle is the only bird to be seen on the highest of our mountain-tops at the dead of winter. Here, at a height of over 4000 feet above sea-level, even the ptarmigan is unable to exist under the polar conditions which prevail from November till May. It is not the cold which drives the birds lower down the hill slopes, but it is the complete absence of food. On these mountain plateaux even the ridges, so exposed that no snow can remain on them, are covered with a thick sheet of ice, and all food is withheld from any bird which should be so hardy as to wish to pass its time at these quarters. But with the eagle the case is different. It is able, without a movement of its great wings, to visit the highest grounds at any season, and on more than one occasion I remember having watched its dark form against those spotless expanses of snow which no one except those familiar with the high hills could imagine to exist on these Islands of ours.

There is no bird that I know which possesses the same strength, the same gracefulness of flight, as the Golden Eagle. I think I first realised the remarkable powers of its soaring on a certain occasion when I was sheltering behind a cairn on a hill-top over 3000 feet above sea-level. A westerly wind was sweeping the hill with such strength that progress had been difficult against it, yet a couple of Golden Eagles, flying dead against the wind, moved past me at a speed of between twenty and thirty miles an hour, without any perceptible motion of the wings. Since then I have often watched the Black Eagle wrestling with the storm, and certainly he is at his best during a day of wild gales and driving showers of rain and sleet. It is on occasions such as these that the King of Birds appears to take delight in pitting his great strength against that of the storm, and, no matter how wild the hurricane, he seems to revel in soaring, grim and inscrutable, in the teeth of the tempest. One such October day I watched him for a while. A westerly gale swept the hills, and so tremendous was the current of air that it was only with difficulty I made my way up the glen. To my right the hillside rose sharp and steep, to a height of nearly 4000 feet, and when first I saw the eagle he was soaring almost motionless against the gale. But after a time, as if in play, the great bird, leaning on the wind, lifted himself somewhat and then, tightly folding his wings, dropped like a stone till he had descended to his former level. And so, rising and falling alternately, the black eagle revelled in the gale and in his great command of flight. The next day I was again on the high hills. The westerly wind still blew, but winter had descended on the corries during the hours of night, and at intervals blizzards of dry powdery snow were swept down the glen, making one seek shelter for the time being behind the nearest rock. During the height of one such squall an eagle crossed the hill-face. Flying in the teeth of the storm, with only an occasional movement of his wings to propel him, the king of the hills moved quickly forward, though by what method he protected his eyes from the blinding snow I cannot say. It may well be that the eagle has the power of drawing across his eye the " third eyelid " on such occasions.

This third eyelid, or Nictitating Membrane, to give it its more scientific title, is a more or less transparent layer of skin which can be moved across the eye in a horizontal direction. My experience has been that the space of time during which the third eyelid covers the eye is merely a fraction of a second, and I do not think it has been investigated whether it is used as a permanent protection, but when an eaglet is frightened or annoyed the third eyelid is repeatedly brought into play. The old saying, to the effect that the eagle has the power of looking straight at the sun, may indeed have its explanation in the Third Eyelid.

But though on a day of storms the power of flight of the eagle is magnificent in its strength, during weather when only a faint breeze rustles the heather on the hilltop the King of Birds is laboured, even ungainly in his movements. At times such as these he resembles in his progress a gigantic rook, beating the air with ponderous flaps of those great wings of his until he reaches an altitude sufficient for him to bring into play his soaring powers. Instances are, indeed, on record of eagles, after feeding heavily on some fallen sheep or deer, being quite unable to rise from the long heather of their sheltered surroundings. To my knowledge there have been two instances of an eagle rising steadily and rapidly from a low level until he was actually lost to view in the blue vault of heaven. In the first case I was privileged to see the great bird execute this extraordinarily impressive manœuvre, and more recently a hill stalker recounted to me his experience, which agreed closely with my own. The glen where the incident happened was a deep one, and rising from it was a precipice close on 1000 feet in height where the eagle and his mate have had their home for generations. For days on end tropical weather had prevailed amongst the high hills. Not a cloud had crossed the sky, and only the lightest of breezes arose with the noon to lighten the burden of the heat. Then one day the north wind crossed the sea, and arrived at the eagle's home. And the eagle

GOLDEN EAGLE SOARING OFF HER EYRIE.

felt the cool arctic breeze and sailed out from his giant rocks which by now were burning hot in the fierce rays of the sun. With his pinions wide outstretched he leaned on the refreshing wind, which bore him strongly upward, without a single stroke of his wings to help him on his way. So he mounted higher and higher till he had risen far above his native hill-top, and was outlined, a mere speck, against the dark blue of the sky. Still upwards he sailed, and for some time longer the watching stalker kept him in view, in the field of his glass. But at length he reached a point at which he was invisible, even by the aid of a telescope. From that point what a gorgeous panorama must have lain spread out before his sight in the light of the summer sun. Even the highest tops were now far far below him, and the river in its windings down the great glen must have appeared as a thin silvery streak.

Another occasion which I recall. The great glen was in shadow, for the sun had already sunk behind Cairn Toul to the west. On the sister hill, Ben Mac Dhui, to the eastward, the sunlight still shone, and as I watched I saw an eagle emerge from the shadow on Cairn Toul. In his true inimitable fashion he was soaring leisurely, proudly, in wide spirals. With each spiral he mounted higher, until at length he reached the rays of the sinking sun, when he was transformed into a veritable eagle of gold, and, as the sun sank still lower, into this gold there came imperceptibly a tinge of pink which lit up each great wing feather of this king of the glen.

The eagle remains with his mate throughout the year, and probably pairs for life. I have on more than one occasion witnessed the meeting between the eagle and his mate. It would almost seem that the time and meeting-place had been agreed upon before they set out on their hunting with the coming of the dawn. Only a short while ago, on a dull and misty October day—a day when the high hills have a special charm—an eagle passed close above my head as I lay amongst the heather. He had come from the highest grounds, from out of the impenetrable mist which had stolen softly across the hill-faces with the strengthening of the day, and he was sailing in a straight line for a hill on the far side of the glen. With the aid of a powerful glass, I marked the eagle until he had reached a point above the far ridge. Here, with a sudden stoop from the higher skies, his mate joined him, and for a time they circled round each other with manifest signs of happiness, before alighting together on the ridge from where they could command the glen.

On fine clear days of summer, when only the lightest of breezes stirs and when the sun shines full on hill and corrie, the Golden Eagle is wont to resort to some favourite perch of his, where he may stand motionless for hours on end digesting his latest meal. I have found interesting things amongst the castings which lie scattered around such a perch. I once saw the remains of a claw of either a grouse or ptarmigan, and, still more curious, a portion of a ptarmigan's egg-shell. The eagle is tireless on the wing, and spends days, especially during fine weather, in crossing and recrossing the mountain-tops and driving the ptarmigan before him. This he does at times for the mere pleasure of the chase, and not because he is anxious to satisfy his appetite upon an unlucky Mountain Grouse. While near the summit of the Cairngorm one fine day towards the end of October I noticed that ptarmigan were present to the leeward side of the cairn—a strong wind was blowing from the south-west—in greater numbers than I ever had seen them at this elevation of 4000 feet. The birds were showing considerable restlessness, and the cause of this restlessness was soon apparent, for an eagle showed himself moving idly over the plateau. There were many ptarmigan on the ground which the eagle commanded in his flight, yet every bird remained quite motionless, crouching low against the hill until the eagle had disappeared from view. Then, somewhat to my surprise, the ptarmigan rose together in a body, and rapidly winged their way in the opposite direction to that taken by the eagle. They evidently had fears that the great bird would return, and that on his return they might not escape so easily as on the first occasion. Later on in this same day, as the last rays of the afterglow were brightening the western sky, I saw outlined against the light a large pack of ptarmigan making their way northwards, with the speed of an express train, over the slopes of Beinn Mheadhoin. The time had long passed when, under ordinary conditions, they would have made themselves comfortable for the night, and I can only imagine that a belated eagle, in quest of his supper, was the cause of this hurried migration in the deepening gloom.

A mid-October evening in the wild glens has a particular charm which no other season of the year can give. On every side one hears the roaring of the stags—hoarse bellowings which fill the corries and re-echo from hill to hill. When we saw the fugitive ptarmigan my friend and I were still a number of miles from our base, and as we tramped on in the darkness the phantom-like forms of big stags with their attendant hinds hurried across the strath before us. Two stags there were which from their deep and powerful voices I took to be the lords of that glen. One of the beasts was on the hillside above us to our left, while the other was on the flat to our right. Both stags had been sending across repeated challenges as we neared their territory. The one on the left I knew, by the peculiar hoarseness of his roarings, to be a splendid " royal " which had annexed to himself a couple of score of hinds, but the beast on the right was a stranger to me.

At our approach, and in order to avoid us, the latter stag moved, with his hinds, across in the direction whence came the excited, almost frenzied roarings of the " royal." I realised that a fight must ensue, and sure enough out of the darkness came almost immediately the crash of antler against antler borne across to us on the stillness of the evening air, though the combatants themselves were hidden by the night. For some minutes we heard blow after blow repeated in rapid succession—until there was sudden quiet and we realised that the vanquished had taken his departure. And now there was but one stag roaring out defiance into the gloom, and the voice was not the hoarse voice of our " royal," but the deep mellow call of his adversary and conqueror. Later on, as we neared our journey's end, the sky lightened eastward and the pale moon showed herself above the brow of the hill. Gradually increasing in the intensity of her rays she mounted higher, and soon sought out, and illuminated, even the shade of the veteran pines which cluster like so many sentinels at the foot of this great glen.

Though the eagle remains constant to his mate throughout the year it is not often that one sees the birds hunting in pairs. On one occasion, however, an eagle and his mate were moving close together over a hill-face. Ptarmigan scattered before them in every direction, but the leading eagle pursued and struck down one of the fugitives. Without heeding the falling ptarmigan he passed on, but his mate, stooping earthwards, seized the prey before it had fallen many yards and continued on her flight, carrying the ptarmigan in her talons. It is, I think, extraordinary how rarely an eagle is seen to capture prey. Time after time he is seen good-naturedly, as it were, pursuing a covey of grouse or ptarmigan, which I imagine are quite unable to see the faintest traces of humour in the situation, but usually, just as he appears about to strike, he swerves suddenly aside and transfers his attentions to another member of the covey.

I have seen an eagle cross and recross a glen when on a hunting expedition, searching a hill-face with considerable care and then with a wide sweep crossing the valley and beating a hill on the opposite side. On such occasions the behaviour of the hunted grouse varies, I think, somewhat. If they happen to be near the actual operations of the eagle they will, in all probability, remain crouching quietly in the shelter of long heather, trusting in their harmonisation with their surroundings to escape the keen eye of their hereditary foe. But should they imagine that they stand a good chance of escape by instant and precipitate flight, they will rise, singly or together, and, flying faster than ever they did at the most sanguinary grouse drive, will endeavour to put as great a distance as possible between themselves and the eagle. One autumn day I was crossing the hills from Perth to Braemar, and at the roadside watched for some time an eagle at his hunting. I had restarted the car and was moving down the glen at a speed of about 25 miles an hour when a covey of grouse shot past me at a velocity greater than that of an express train. There was a whole gale of wind blowing behind them, and I calculate that their speed of flight cannot have been less than 100 miles an hour. As they passed I looked back and saw the eagle still searching a hillside quietly. Either he had not noticed the fugitives, or else he realised that pursuit was useless and so let well alone.

I think it is possible to tell, by the flight of grouse and ptarmigan, whether they are seeking to escape their hereditary enemy, the eagle, or their more recent but much more deadly enemy, man. As a general rule, when the eagle is the cause of disturbance the grouse fly at a greater height above ground and their flight is more precipitate and aimless than when man is the cause of alarm. It is of interest to realise how strong is the hereditary instinct of dread felt towards the eagle, and in obedience to this instinct grouse will cheerfully face in great numbers a whole line of guns which must spell death to them, rather than approach the locality where the eagle has been spied. I was travelling on the Highland Railway recently, from Inverness to Perth, and just at the county march, where the line borders on the 1500 feet level, I saw a grouse cross the line above the train, flying high and with a distinctive rocking flight. I was almost certain that an eagle, and not the Highland express, was the cause of alarm, and sure enough, on looking out of the opposite window, I saw the enemy there sailing far off above the top of a neighbouring hill. As well as striking down its prey in mid air, the eagle at times captures, or attempts to capture, grouse and ptarmigan on the ground, but that it is not invariably successful in this, I think the following incident will show.

One winter's afternoon I watched a pair of eagles on a grouse moor where they had been seen regularly for some weeks. One of the eagles had apparently retired to roost on a heather-clad hillside when a grouse which I disturbed crossed the burn and alighted almost on the top of the eagle. The latter immediately rose and made a stoop at the grouse but missed its mark, striking itself, with the impact of its descent, heavily against the hillside. Somewhat dazed, the great bird thereupon rose, and mounting in spirals made its way across the hill till it was lost to sight.

The principal prey of the eagle in this country is the Red Grouse, but where mountain hares are numerous on the hillsides there is no doubt they are taken in preference to the more active birds. There is one nesting site of a pair of eagles that I know of—in the heart of a grouse moor —where, every year that the birds visit the eyrie for the purpose of nidification, the eggs are taken and sometimes the hen bird is captured on the nest. The keepers have, I admit, a strong argument on their side to support their line of conduct, but I really believe that the birds in this instance prey very largely on the blue hares which are more numerous, hereabouts, than on any other hills that I know of. This partiality of the eagle for hares can easily be understood, for poor puss has but little chance of escaping her winged adversary unless there is rocky ground near. Once amongst the rocks, however, she is comparatively safe. An instance is on record of an eagle losing a hare under a large rock. The fugitive was hard pressed when she made for this place of refuge, and on seeing her disappear the eagle seemed at a loss how to act. He hopped from one side of the rock to another; then apparently realising that he was powerless under such annoying circumstances spread his wings and sailed quietly away. A different state of affairs prevails, however, when the pursued hare seeks cover amongst bushes or undergrowth, for then the eagle routs out the fugitive by repeated blows from his wings upon the sheltering bush.

Having captured and killed their prey, eagles are sometimes seen to drop their victim from a great height and, stooping like lightning after the falling body, reach and secure it long before it has touched the ground. Sometimes, though seldom, it is true, they are too late in their pursuit, and a veteran highland stalker told me an interesting story of how he once discovered a freshly-killed hare lying on the snow with no footprints of any kind around. It had undoubtedly been dropped by an eagle, and personally I have more than once found ptarmigan on the ground under circumstances which led me to suppose that in these cases also the eagle was the culprit.

The eagle and the hill fox have similar tastes, and between them is, as a rule, an armed neutrality. But at times the eagle will not hesitate to bear off a young fox cub to his eyrie, and I have before now seen the remains of a desperate encounter on the hill, with the fox's fur scattered abroad in every direction. A certain interesting fight between a fox and an eagle may be set down here. The eagle was devouring the carcase of a blue hare when a fox sprang from the surrounding heather and seized the great bird by the wing. A well-contested struggle ensued in which the eagle made a desperate attempt to defend itself with its claws and succeeded in extricating itself from its enemy's grasp, but before it had time to escape Reynard seized it by the breast and seemed more determined than ever. The eagle made another attempt to overpower its antagonist by striking with its wings, but that would not compel the aggressor to quit its hold. At last the eagle succeeded in raising the fox from the ground, and for a few minutes Reynard was suspended by his own jaws between heaven and earth. Although now placed in an unfavourable position for fighting his courage did not forsake him, as he firmly kept his hold and seemed to make several attempts to bring the eagle down, but he soon found the strong wings of the eagle were capable of raising him, and that there was no way of escape unless the bird should alight somewhere. The eagle made a straight ascent and rose to a considerable height in the air. After struggling for a time Reynard was obliged to quit his grasp, and descended much quicker than he had gone up. He was dashed to the earth, where he lay struggling in the agonies of death. The eagle made his escape, but appeared weak from exhaustion and loss of blood.

A stalker of my acquaintance was " spying " a certain hillside when his glass rested upon a fox curled up comfortably asleep on a bare patch surrounded by heather. An eagle, being apparently attracted by the bare hillside, swept earthward and was just about to alight when he spied Reynard lying asleep within a few feet of him. His surprise—and alarm—were great, and he shot sky-wards again with considerable speed, but the fox merely raised his head inquiringly and then resumed his nap. I heard recently of an eagle being disturbed in a Scots fir just as it had commenced to feed on a magpie which it had captured. The eagle on the approach of the stalker sailed away out of sight, but somewhat exceptionally, I think, returned later to finish its victim.

St. John in his now classical work on *Wild Sports in the Highlands,* states that the Martin and the Wild Cat are the eagle's favourite morsels. I much doubt, how-ever, whether St. John was correct in his statement—at all events both of these animals are so scarce that they are negligible at the present day as an article of food. An eagle has been known to stoop at a hare pursued by hounds and carry it off a hundred yards before them. It is said to attack Gannets, but I much doubt whether this is really the case, and more than likely the observer confused the aggressor with a specimen of the White-tailed Eagle, which is a frequenter of our coast-line. The Golden Eagle is almost entirely an inland nester in this country, and as the Gannet never flies across the most minute point of land, in the ordinary course of events the two birds are unlikely ever to come to close quarters. The Golden Eagle will sometimes capture and devour black game, but owing to the habits of these birds—they frequent thick pine woods as a rule—they usually succeed in avoid-ing the attacks of the eagle by diving headlong amongst the sheltering pine branches.

Though the eagle undoubtedly prefers to capture his prey for himself, he is not above descending to carrion, and often becomes gorged on the remains of a dead stag or sheep. I do not think, however, that his young are ever fed on dead meat—they always have their provender provided from day to day in a perfectly fresh state.

The Black Eagle nests early. In January he may be seen assisting his mate in the repairing of his eyrie by carrying to it large pine branches, and this repairing or building of the nest goes on till mid-March, at which time the birds which are nesting in the less exposed localities begin to lay. One 23rd of March I visited an eyrie situated in a Scots fir in a deer forest. The elevation for the eagle was rather a low one—about 1400 feet—and I found that the hen bird was already covering her eggs, though she did not allow of near approach. The eagle utilises two kinds of nesting-places in Scotland. It chooses for the construction of its eyrie either an ancient tree commanding a wide outlook, or a ledge on some precipice or steep hillside. Towards the west coast of Scotland its eyrie is rarely found in a tree, but in the central deer forests, where most of my notes have been obtained, the two nesting situations are about equally utilised. I think those eagles which build in trees have rather a better chance of rearing their broods in safety than those which construct their eyries on ledges of rocks. To begin with, the birds choosing the former situation are independent of the weather because, no matter what depth of snow may cover the ground, they can build their eyrie and cover their eggs without fear of the storm. On the other hand, it is sometimes impossible for the birds nesting on a ledge of rock to approach their eyrie till well into the spring, so great an accumulation of winter's snow may cover it during the month of March. I also think that the young eaglets hatched on a rock are more liable to fall from the nest. For sanitary purposes they are in the habit of approaching the extreme edge of the eyrie, and on one occasion I found a youthful eaglet in a most precarious position, and maintaining its hold by one leg only. I replaced it in the centre of the nest, but next time I visited the eyrie it had fallen to the ground fifty feet below. Of its companion—there were originally two eaglets—there was no sign, so I imagine the fall proved fatal to it. The parent eagles had built a rough nest round their surviving youngster, in order, I suppose, to show any marauding fox or stoat that the eaglet was not abandoned to the unkind world. I do not think eaglets are so liable to fall from trees because they probably realise more fully, from the swaying of the tree in the wind, the fall that awaits them if they should lose their hold of the nest. Again, eagles nesting on trees have, if the situation of the tree be well chosen, an uninterrupted outlook on every side, while those nesting on rocks have an excellent view in one direction but can usually be closely approached from above without their being rendered suspicious of danger.

The period of incubation is about six weeks—perhaps a day or two under—and towards the end of her first period of self-denial as a mother the eagle becomes most reluctant to leave her eggs. Under such conditions she will put her head over the side of her eyrie and glare fiercely at the intruder, repeatedly rolling the third eyelid across her eye the while. Before the eaglets have filled the eggs with their small down-clad bodies the mother eagle is full of suspicions, and will leave the nest while danger is still some way off. On one occasion, however, an eagle of my acquaintance sat so closely, even during the first few days of incubation, that I was able to watch her at close quarters through the glass. I remember remarking on the dark colour of her plumage ; so that when I visited the eyrie five weeks later on, I was surprised to see an eagle several shades lighter than my former friend sail out over the glen from her nesting-tree. Of course it is possible that this was the mate doing his period of covering the eggs, but the stalker who was with me at the time was emphatic that the eagle, during her six weeks of close sitting, invariably became lighter in her plumage. In the ordinary course of events the young eagles have their plumage of dark brown, almost black, feathers, while the veterans wear a dress of light tawny colour.

The nest of the Golden Eagle is a structure of considerable size, and with every year of its tenancy becomes increasingly bulky. If built on a tree, its foundations usually consist of large fir branches, some of them as thick as a man's wrist, while towards the top of the nest green branches from the same species of tree are also utilised. These branches are invariably pulled from the pine itself by the eagles, as a dead branch is never used for the top of the nest. In nine eyries out of ten one finds, lining the shallow depression that is to receive the eggs, leaves from a grass-like plant known to scientists as *Luzula sylvatica*. I remember how, as a small person, this plant used to be pointed out to me as the Sword grass. As to the correctness of this term I am in doubts, but certainly the edges of the grass are sharp out of the ordinary, and if they are drawn across the hand they cause blood to flow. Sometimes *Luzula sylvatica* is used as a lining along with dried fronds of the bracken, and I have seen an eyrie containing not a leaf of *Luzula*. I must say, however, that in this instance the nest was built on an open hillside, with no woods anywhere in the vicinity, so the eagles had little opportunity of gathering the " grass " which grows as a rule in sheltered and wooded localities. A few sprays of the Cranberry—*Oxycoccus*—and the Crowberry—*Empetrum nigrum*—usually complete the furnishing of the home. The eagles are fond of decorating their eyries. On more than one occasion I found a bamboo cane in the nest, and once a red rubber ring. A pair of eagles which had a thriving eaglet in their eyrie were in the habit of bringing to the nest, at intervals of a day or two, young and delicate raspberry shoots which they thought—and rightly—improved the look of their home.

Although as a rule the lining which receives the eggs is soft and comfortable, I once saw in an eyrie a large stick, nearly the thickness of my wrist, against which the eggs were lying, and which one would have thought must have caused incessant inconvenience to the brooding eagle.

The eggs are two in number. Occasionally three are recorded, but in the numbers of eyries I have examined I have never seen the latter number, nor have I heard of anyone who has done so, and out of over fifty eyries robbed between 1870 and 1895, only three contained three eggs. The eggs are of a dirty white ground colour, and are blotched and spotted with reddish brown. It is a noteworthy and interesting fact that one of the eggs is invariably more lightly spotted and marked than its fellow. It has been my experience that when two eaglets are reared, one is a cock, the other a hen, and it is possible that this marking of the eggs may have something to do with the sex of the bird, though I am afraid this theory is opposed to the scientific one that the sex of the bird is determined only just before the hatching of the egg. As far as I know, however, the subject has never in this case been investigated. Some eggs of the eagle are strikingly handsome, but others have hardly any markings on them at all, and I believe that many of the clutches taken from Archangel are pure white.

It is quite remarkable what long-continued exposure the eggs of the Golden Eagle will stand. I have known of a case when an eagle's eyrie was discovered on a day of severe frost and periodic snow-squalls. The mother bird was sitting closely, but was put off her eggs, and I think it is no exaggeration to say that she remained away

B

from her nest at least two hours, possibly longer, yet one of the eggs hatched out successfully, though the other—whether owing to this or to another cause—was addled when I climbed to the nest a month later.

On fine sunny days the eagle sometimes leaves her eyrie for a few minutes, to stretch herself and perhaps to reconnoitre also. I was once watching an eyrie from a distance of 200 yards, when I saw the eagle leave her nest and rise almost perpendicularly into the air. This evolution of hers caused the greatest perturbation amongst the grouse of the hillside who rose in a body and fled at top speed over the brow of the hill. Having assured herself that all was well, the eagle settled herself on her eggs and fell so fast asleep that even when I stood at the foot of the tree and whistled, it took her some time to realise all was not well and to thrust her head inquiringly over the edge of the nest.

A season rarely passes without the parent eagle experiencing at least one storm of snow during her period of incubation. If her nest is built on a tree, such a storm, as I said before, has no danger for her, but if she has her eyrie on a rock, she may be obliged to leave her eggs owing to the great depth of snow which is drifted in upon the sheltered ledge by the force of the storm. I have certainly never known this to happen, but I once saw an eagle covering her eyrie when an average depth of over two feet of snow lay on the hillside ; and if this great storm had been accompanied by heavy drifting, I doubt whether the eagle could have held her ground. There are many ideal nesting sites for the Golden Eagle among the gloomy precipices of the Cairngorms, but these sites are not utilised—for the reason, I think, that the snow lies too deeply on the rocks during the months of March and April. There is only one eagle's nest I know of at a greater elevation than 3000 feet, and I suspect that this nest is now tenantless, for I have not seen the eagles near.

The Golden Eagle is not, I think, inclined to choose a nesting site because of its inaccessibility, for I have known an eyrie to be placed almost on the ground; and there is on record an instance of an old woman once walking into an eagle's nest and carrying off the eggs in her apron. Often a ledge seems to be chosen from the fact that a sapling birch or rowan is growing on it, and this is utilised as a support for the foundations of the eyrie. That such a tree is called upon to stand a considerable strain is realised when it is stated that an eyrie may attain a width of from five to six feet. A certain pair of eagles have been singularly unfortunate in their nesting of late. A heavy storm of wet snow broke down the eyrie which they had occupied for many years in succession. The eagles thereupon moved to an ancient home of theirs in a rock hard by, but ill-fortune still pursued them, for a large heather fire on the hillside beneath burnt so fiercely that it ran up the eagles' rock and completely gutted the eyrie. The eagles now decided to trust their treasures to the care of a tree once more, and constructed a new eyrie on a fir near their fallen nest. The nest was built and the eggs laid, but it is probable that the foundation of the eyrie was faulty, and that one of the equinoctial gales overthrew it. At all events, it was found lying on the heather, and the broken eggs beside it. The stalker who made the discovery told me that the dried-up remnants of yolk showed that incubation was not far advanced, so it is possible— though I think unlikely—that the eagles built a new nest and laid a second clutch of eggs in another part of the forest.

It is, perhaps, unjust to condemn from circumstantial evidence alone, but I have a shrewd suspicion that the eggs of the Golden Eagle are sometimes stolen by the wary and resourceful Hoodie Crow. I have known a clutch of eagle's eggs disappear mysteriously, and though it is possible this may have been due to human agency, it is more probable that the hoodie was the culprit. A stalker once wrote to me that he had found, immediately beneath the nest of a grey crow, a small portion of an egg which he took to be a turkey's. To the casual observer there is really surprisingly little difference between an eagle's egg-shell and a turkey's, provided only a small portion is seen, except that the eagle's egg-shell is considerably rougher and thicker. Now since not a single representative of the turkey tribe was to be found for many miles round the grey crow's nest, I am inclined to think that the hoodie had succeeded in extracting an egg from the eyrie of a pair of Golden Eagles near during the absence of the owners.

It is during the last days of April that the earliest-hatched eaglets first see the light of day from behind the sheltering feathers of their mother. They are clad in warm coats of white down, and have surprisingly shrill and penetrating voices for small people of such tender age. They are provided with a little white diamond on the convex part of the bill to enable them to break through the strong shell of their prison. I should say the average date for the first eaglet to emerge from its egg is April 29th—that is, for eagles nesting between 1500 and 2000 foot levels. The second egg does not hatch out till at least a couple of days later. The eaglets are supplied liberally with food from the first, but from this generous larder they are allowed only the most tender morsels until, with the strengthening of spring, they become more robust, and are permitted to feed, more or less, on what they like. The liver of a rabbit or hare or the most appetising and easily-digested portion of a grouse are offered the baby by its parents, and it is not until it has reached

the age of a month that it is allowed to consume the
entrails of the prey. When the eagles are young, they are
fed twice a day—at daybreak and about five in the afternoon, and at the latter hour the parent eagle may often
be seen winging her way back from a hunting expedition,
carrying in her talons a fat grouse, which gives her a curious
appearance, not unlike a miniature aeroplane.

The most interesting sidelight I ever had on the
domestic affairs of the eagle was just at sunrise one July
morning, in a glen where a pair of these birds have nested
in a fir tree from time immemorial. The eyrie had originally contained two birds, but the cock eaglet had taken
his departure a day or two before my visit, and was awaiting to be fed somewhere amongst the long heather below
the nest. I could see, from my hiding-place, one of the
parent eagles standing on guard on the hill-top. The
morning wind ruffled its feathers as it stood there on the
skyline, and from time to time it cast its glance upwards,
evidently expecting the arrival of its mate. At last it
soared up, and I saw the second bird arriving from what
had evidently been an early morning foray. The foray
had been unsuccessful, however, and for a time the two
birds circled round each other as if discussing future
plans, for a hungry eaglet yelping in the nest below brought
home to them the fact that a grouse or hare must be
provided at all cost. Soon a new plan of campaign was
formed, and the bird which had previously been on guard
set out westward, flying high, and evidently making for
hunting-grounds a considerable distance off. Its mate
accompanied it a short distance, and then, sweeping round,
returned to the hillside and took up guard above the
nest.

It is possible, I think, by paying repeated visits to an
eyrie, to tame the eaglets to a certain extent. There was
one eaglet which, after a time, used to feed from my hand.

I first tempted him with choice morsels from a grouse in the nest, and then offered him a piece of banana skin, which he swallowed philosophically. This bird was in a neighbourhood much infested by ants, and during the time I watched him many of these aggravating insects were crawling up and down his legs. Beyond regarding them with an intent and curious stare, however, the eagle in no way tried to rid himself of the ants, for he seemed to regard them as one of the annoying necessities of existence. A butterfly flitting near interested him, and the movements of a hind in the wood below also distracted his attention for a while, but he betrayed for the most part a bored expression, and once yawned heavily. As I was leaving, his mother suddenly appeared over the rock bearing in her talons a grouse for the youngster's mid-day meal. The eaglet at once became most excited and called repeatedly, but the parent bird, on seeing me, shot up into the air and, to the intense annoyance of her child, disappeared from sight.

The range of prey brought to the eyrie by a pair of Golden Eagles during the nesting season is great. The two staple articles of food, however, are the Red Grouse and the Blue Hare, though where rabbits are plentiful they are also brought to the nest in numbers. One never sees an entire hare at the eyrie, only the haunches, so that possibly the head and body are consumed by the parent bird on the spot where the victim was captured. Curiously enough, I have never found the remains of a ptarmigan in an eyrie, which is the more noteworthy from the fact that some of the eagles I have studied do their hunting as much on ptarmigan ground as on grouse moors. I have seen the tail of a squirrel in an eyrie, and also on one occasion the remains of a stoat. Sometimes small birds, such as the Meadow Pipit, are brought as food for the young. Deer, calves, and lambs are taken also,

GOLDEN EAGLET NEARLY A MONTH OLD.

The wing feathers are just commencing to sprout.

GOLDEN EAGLET.

This picture was taken about five weeks before the bird left the eyrie.

though I cannot say I have ever come across the remains of either of these animals in an eyrie.

I believe the eagle is more destructive to lambs on the west coast than in the central districts, partly, no doubt, owing to the more extensive sheep farms towards the western sea-board. From one such farm thirty-five lambs were carried off in a single season, so it can be realised that between eagle and shepherd there exists little friendly feeling. There is an instance recorded of an eagle carrying a lamb no less than two miles, and then dropping it none the worse for its adventure. It is also related that a poor man in Ireland once tided over a season of famine by taking daily some of the food the parent eagles brought for their young. He succeeded thus in providing for himself, his wife, and his family, for several months, and by clipping the wings of the young birds, protracted their stay in the nest.

In this country a couple of grouse and a mountain hare would be held as quite a satisfactorily-proportioned larder, but in an eyrie in Germany the remains of three hundred duck and forty hares were once found—if report be credited. On a certain occasion the tables were turned on the bird of prey, for a cat which was carried by the eagle to her eyrie in an apparently dead condition is said to have revived and eaten the eaglets during the parents' absence.

Up to the age of three weeks the eaglets are still clad entirely in down, and there is no sign of the permanent feathers. Once these appear, however, they grow rapidly, and after three more weeks the down is visible only in patches. It is about the neck that the downy covering lingers longest, and an eaglet, after having assumed the full plumage on the other parts of the body, still has the feathers of the neck in an unopened and rudimentary condition. In its early youth the eaglet has no fear of the human intruder, though maybe if it becomes cold owing to the protracted absence of its mother, it will yell repeatedly and lustily. I once quieted such a youngster by placing a freshly-killed grouse to windward of it, to act as a screen against the cold north-easter which was sweeping the glen.

The Golden Eagle has a curious and quite erroneous reputation for bravery where the defence of its young is concerned which is difficult to explain. It is always a disagreeable duty to shatter a reputation—and a firmly-grounded reputation, too—but I am afraid that the eagle shows, what to us at all events appears to be a philosophic indifference as to the fate of its young, and as for attacking the intruder at its eyrie, well, such a thing appears never so much as to enter its head. I have had my camera set up on the edge of an eyrie and have photographed the eaglets in various positions while the mother eagle remained quietly, and seemingly without anxiety, perched on a rock on the hill face opposite. Whether she by this time—I had on several occasions visited the eyrie before—realised that I had no evil intentions towards her children, I do not know ; but she was either trustful or indifferent.

The traditions handed down in the Highlands of eagles carrying children to the eyrie are largely mythical. No doubt such cases have occurred, but they are due to the carelessness of mothers who have left their babies un-attended in some out-of-the-way spot. Under these cir-cumstances what can be more natural than that an eagle on his hunting operations should spy what seems to him to be a dainty morsel, and should immediately stoop down and carry it off to his young ? We cannot well blame him. Sometimes, during recent years, such cases have been reported in the papers, but have been proved, one and all, to be without foundation.

In Spain the wild goats have a relentless enemy in the eagle, for the birth of the kids coincides with the period when the birds of prey have young, and the kids are used largely in feeding the eaglets.

A mysterious fate often overtakes one of the eaglets in an eyrie when two birds are hatched out. Various theories have been put forward to account for this disappearance. Highland stalkers will tell you that the mother eagle herself does away with the more weakly of her chicks, or even that a battle takes place between the two small eaglets and that the less powerful is killed in the conflict. I imagine that food has a great deal to do with the disappearance of one of the eaglets. Sometimes, too, one of the birds probably falls out of the nest, but it is certainly noteworthy that no small body is ever found.

The eagle is essentially a bird of silence. When leaving her eyrie the hen rarely utters a single cry, and not even when the young are in danger does she use her call note. There are exceptions, however, and I have once or twice heard her call, several times in succession, as she sailed out from the nest. The eagle almost invariably flies right away when disturbed from her eyrie, but on a certain occasion that I shall always remember, the great bird displayed remarkable tameness. She left her eggs with obvious reluctance, and then flew only a short distance, to a dead branch of a pine rather over 100 yards distant. After waiting a time, she actually flew straight towards me, settling on a tree close by. Her anxiety as to the safety of her eggs was great, and she searched the sky eagerly, expectantly, for her mate, on whom she evidently relied for support. But no dark form against the clouds rewarded her gaze, and she gave utterance to a succession of curious barking cries quite unlike anything I have ever heard before or since, until she again took wing, and this time sailed right out of sight.

Most of the pairs of eagles of my acquaintance have two or even three eyries, which they use in rotation, in different parts of the same glen ; and it is interesting to know that Col. Verner found this to be the case in Spain also. Sometimes, I think, one of these spare eyries is used as a larder, for I once found the hind quarters of a hare freshly killed lying in a nest which contained no eggs. During the early months of spring the eagles appear to be undecided as to which of their homes they should occupy for the approaching nesting season. They visit them in turn, and add a few green pine branches to each eyrie, in order, I imagine, to make it plain to any wandering and homeless eagles that the glen is already occupied. There is one rock I know of where there are no less than four eyries within 50 yards of each other, all the property of the same pair of eagles.

Owing to their extensive hunting operations a pair of eagles will not allow a second pair to set up house within three or four miles, at the nearest, and as a result the Golden Eagle can never become really numerous anywhere. However, I am quite sure that in the Highlands he is holding his own, and as long as he does not encroach too much on grouse ground he is rarely disturbed.

The eaglets remain in the eyrie for a period of nine weeks, so that they make their first flight about the 8th of July. The date of this flight is extremely regular, and the earliest day on which I have known the young eagles to leave the nest was July 5th. On this date I made an expedition to an eyrie built on an ancient Scots fir at a height of 1800 feet above sea-level. After a spell of cold and misty weather an anti-cyclone had brought with it cloudless skies and light, variable breezes, and as I moved up the glen the sun shone with great power. The eyrie was soon located, and the two eaglets, a cock and a hen, were seen to be almost full-fledged. I had hoped to obtain some photographs of them in their eyrie, but I had not reached a point half-way up the tree—and a none too easy climb it was—when both eaglets took wing simultaneously, and flying side by side, made for the foot of the glen. Their flight was somewhat unstable, and they gradually sank earthwards until they came to ground at the side of the hill burn which drains the glen. Here, after a certain amount of searching, I discovered the hen eaglet standing quietly in a small tributary of the main stream, and, after having photographed her, I set about looking for the cock. He had wandered off up the hillside, and I found him amongst long heather, where successful photography was precluded. The difficulty of transporting my subject to more suitable surroundings was overcome by my divesting myself of my kilt and carrying the eagle a distance of some two hundred yards in the folds of the feileadh beag. Far from struggling, my captive remained quite quiet and passive during the journey, and ultimately I placed him and his sister on a large dead branch, where I photographed them together. They could be distinguished from fully-matured birds only by the shortness of their tails and by the unformed feathers on the neck. Though on this occasion they could not rise from level ground, their wing power had increased so rapidly, that when, nine days later, I revisited the spot, I found the only bird I saw so strong in his flight that he would not allow me to approach within fifty yards of him, but soared out over the hill in masterly fashion.

Young eagles invariably show considerable powers of flight at the first, but I think the most remarkable performance was given by an eaglet which had been brought up in an eyrie on a steep hill face overlooking a deep glen. The eaglet left its nest on its first flight one gloomy morning in mid-July and treated me to an exhibition of flying which was quite noteworthy. Sailing out from the eyrie, the eaglet at first had considerable difficulty in maintaining its balance, but as its confidence increased, so did its power of flight. I imagined, from my previous experience of first flights, that the eagle would gradually descend, and would come to earth somewhere on the opposite hill face, but, on the contrary, it maintained its level well, and made off, powerfully and easily, up the glen until lost to view round a bend in the burn. A few days later I visited another eyrie, also on a rock. The nest was empty, but there were ample signs that the youngster had left only a short time previously, and as we stood beside the nest he sailed heavily across the strath and alighted 200 yards from us on the hillside opposite. I wished to secure some photographs of him, and commenced a careful stalk, but I had reached a point still 100 yards from him when he rose and flapped his way down the glen. For over an hour I pursued him backwards and forwards, but although his flights were less than half a mile—he had obviously had little practice, and there were no air currents to buoy him up—he never permitted of a nearer approach than 50 yards.

For some time after they leave the nest the young eagles remain with the parent birds, by which they are initiated into the mysteries of capturing the timid hare and the quick-flying grouse. All that summer they hunt together, but during the opening months of the new year, if not before, the parent eagles turn on their offspring and drive them from the glen where they spent the earliest days of their life. Mr. Abel Chapman relates the following extraordinary occurrence from Spain. He shot a Serpent Eagle, and in this bird found the almost entire remains of a young nestling Golden Eagle—a thing almost unbelievable were it not for the authority and standing of the writer. The eagles in Spain seem to be similar to those in this country as regards their habits. The eggs are, as here, laid in mid-March, but if report is correct,

the young birds leave the eyrie as early as June. One
eyrie measured was no less than eight feet deep ; it was
built of sticks, was lined with Esparto grass and adorned
with green ivy leaves and twigs of *Abies pinsapo*.
The nest is almost invariably placed on a crag in Spain,
a tree being rarely selected. However, Mr. R. B. Lodge
mentions that between Serajevo and Gravosa he saw a huge
nest of a Golden Eagle in a small tree not ten feet from
the ground. In Spain, too, a Golden Eagle has been known
to appropriate for itself a discarded eyrie of Bonelli's Eagle.

In Scotland I once saw an eyrie in a comparatively
small birch tree, where the eagles successfully reared a
single young one despite the fact that the eyrie was only
a hundred yards from a right of way along which a number
of pedestrians passed. On the same tree occupied by a
pair of eagles was found, on one occasion, a jay's nest,
a dove's nest, and several nests of sparrows. I have more
than once seen Coal Titmice flitting unconcernedly around
an occupied eyrie, and imagine that they may even make
their nests in some of the holes near the foundations of
the eagles' nest. The eggs of the eagle are variable in
shape, but it may be said the dimensions vary from 3·23
by 2·59 to 2·85 by 2·16 inches. This is taking the average
of a large number of clutches.

For some months after leaving the eyrie the eaglets
lack that gracefulness and command of flight which is
possessed by their parents. One October I watched a
young eagle of that year making its way over the plateau
of Lochnagar. A ptarmigan rose near the line of its
flight and it swerved off, appearing to have in its mind
the capture of the fugitive, but its efforts in that direction were indifferent and the ptarmigan made its escape
without difficulty.

Quite apart from its inferior powers of flight, a young
eagle can be distinguished from its parents by a patch

of white on either wing, and from the fact of its having
the basal three-fourths of the tail white, while only the
remaining fourth is a rich brown. So marked is this
feature that the young has obtained the distinct name of
Ring-tailed Eagle.

The age at which a young eagle reaches maturity is
doubtful. Booth put this period at five or six years, which
does not appear to be excessive when the longevity of the
eagle is taken into consideration, for it seems to be a
general rule that the longer lived the bird, the more slowly
does it reach its prime ; and the Solan Goose, which probably does not exceed or even reach the age of an eagle, takes
quite five years to assume the full nesting plumage. It is
true that the age which the eagle attains in the wild state
must remain largely a matter for conjecture, but there is
an instance of one having lived 104 years in captivity.

Though the eagle has no enemy worthy of his steel,
yet there are adversaries which, though impotent as
individuals, are still able to cause the King of Birds a
good deal of annoyance when they attack in jostling
crowds. Chief among these annoying adversaries is the
Grey or Hoodie Crow. The hoodie has its home in the
wild deer forests, where the stalkers are unwilling to molest
it, and it uses every opportunity of mobbing the eagle.
It must be a humiliating and unenviable position to be
swooped at by a score of yelling black pests, but the eagle
under such circumstances has never been known to forget
his position as being of royal blood. With ease he might
pursue and strike down, one after the other, the Grey
Crows, but he never betrays by the least sign or movement that he is even aware of their presence. With a
young eagle, however, the case is different, and I once saw
such a bird driven to take shelter in a wood by the repeated attacks of the hoodies. Even after the object
of their hostility was perched on a dead branch the crows

still swooped down one after the other, but failing to make the eagle move on at length gave up their attacks. These unwelcome attentions from members of the crow family are not confined to this country, for Mr. Abel Chapman puts it on record that in Spain the eagle is mobbed by Choughs. The raven is much more formidable than the hoodie as an adversary, and though in the part of the Highlands with which I am most familiar it is not present in sufficient numbers to be worth reckoning on, still I heard of an instance, on the west coast, where the ravens on a certain deer forest increased to such an extent that they drove every eagle from the district.

The rook has rarely a chance of mobbing the eagle, but that it does avail itself of an opportunity when such is presented to it is borne out by the following incident. On the county march between Perth and Aberdeen I saw an eagle sailing down the corrie at the head of which its eyrie was built. It was pursued by a number of small antagonists which I imagined at first to be hoodies, but as pursuers and pursued approached nearer, I realised that a number of common rooks were harrying the great bird of prey. Time after time they stooped at the eagle, but I noticed that they exercised a certain amount of discretion in their attacks, for they rarely came within reach of their adversary's bill or claws, and contented themselves for the most part in stooping at the outstretched wings. It seems to be an invariable rule in nature that the pursued never turns upon its pursuers, and this is well illustrated, I think, with the eagle. The latter is chased by all kinds of small birds, notably by Missel Thrushes, and yet, as I have said, I have never seen or heard of one retaliating on the smaller assailants.

The Golden Eagle not infrequently attacks red deer, and I was once witness of a picturesque incident in this connection while crossing the Larig Ghruamach pass which links Aviemore in Inverness-shire with Braemar in Aberdeen-shire. At the top of the pass where the river Dee has its origin I rested awhile, and soon I saw my friend the eagle sailing, in the teeth of the cold northerly breeze, across the hill face of Ben Mac Dhui. All at once he hesitated for a moment in his flight, then closing his wings shot earthward, but checked himself and moved forward again. A thick mist was rolling up, so that I was unable to follow the eagle beyond the point where he entered the cloud. I was anxious to see what had been the cause of his sudden pause and stoop, and on turning the glass on to the spot, I saw a herd of stags looking up uneasily towards the eagle. The bird in its passing had seen the herd and had stooped playfully just to bring the beasts to the alert. A few hours later I met a stalker, and on my relating the episode to him, he told me that an eagle—in all probability the same bird—had been seen a few days before to drive a herd of deer before it up a hillside by swooping down at them repeatedly. This manœuvre caused a good deal of inconvenience to a stalker who was also after these same stags, for the eagle was driving the deer in a direction less favourable for the stalk.

From the following incident which was related to me, it would appear that a single roebuck has more courage than a whole herd of stags. An eagle, sailing over a hill-side, spied a roe feeding, and swooped down on the animal. The roe, far from showing alarm, stood erect on his hind legs and beat out vigorously with his fore-feet with great anger. The eagle thereupon turned its attentions to a herd of stags which were grazing near. The red deer at the first " stoop " of the eagle thought discretion to be the better part of valour and moved quickly off over the hill. One can imagine that after the incident there was one very proud roebuck in the forest. Once on Ben Alder an eagle was seen to hover above a herd of deer and then to pounce on to a calf. The animal's mother immediately rushed to the spot and threw herself on the eagle, whereupon hind, calf, and eagle rolled over and over down the hillside. On releasing itself the eagle flew off, somewhat shaken, and the life of the calf was saved.

There is a story that once an eagle was attacking a hind, which made for a thick wood. As she ran through the plantation at top speed, the eagle, in its endeavours to bring her to a standstill, grasped a branch with one of its feet while holding the back of the hind firmly with the other. But its strength was useless against the weight and impetus of the quickly-moving deer, and it was torn asunder as the hind pressed forward.

There is no doubt that eagles use a great deal of intelligence in their efforts to encompass the destruction of a stag or hind. They realise that they are powerless to kill the best in fair fight, so they attempt to achieve this end by strategy. Choosing out a young or sickly deer, they endeavour, first to separate it from the herd, and then to drive it over some rock where it will either kill itself outright or else lie in a more or less defenceless state and fall an easy victim. The eagle hovers about the head of the unfortunate animal, buffeting it with its wings, and endeavours so to blind it that it stumbles over the rock unknowingly.

It is remarkable, considering how many traps are set for hoodies and foxes, that an eagle is only occasionally captured in this way. In a forest on the borders of Forfar and Aberdeen an eagle was found in such a trap. The bird had only just died when discovered—but not from want of food, for the remains of two freshly-killed grouse and a blue hare were lying within reach. They had evidently been brought by the eagle's mate for its unfortunate companion, and the incident more fully brings out, I

C

think, that the eagle is, of all the birds, the one most
nearly approaching human intelligence.

There is an old Gaelic narrative of how the birds once
upon a time agreed to make king the one which should fly
highest. The eagle expected to win, but the wren chal-
lenged it. The eagle, soaring out of sight into the sky,
cried out, " Cait am bheit thu nis a Dhreathan duinn ? "
" Where are you now, little wren ? " But the wren had
secretly perched on the eagle's back before he had started,
and now flew up still higher, calling as he flew, " Fad fad
os do cheann." " Far, far above you." So the wren was
made king. I was recently conversing with an old Highland stalker on the eagle, and he assured me that it
renewed its youth every seven years, and had indeed
discovered the secret of perennial youthfulness. He stated
that the eagle's bill is renewed every seven years, and with
the renewal of the bill the whole body is renovated also.
A quaint theory this of the old hill-man's, yet I believe
this idea is widely prevalent among the older generation.

Fights between eagles are rare—they seem to rise
superior to the quarrels of lower humanity—yet on one
occasion an eagle was captured by a sheep dog whilst
fighting on the ground with a rival. Another instance
occurred of two eagles fighting so savagely that they
became interlocked, and could not separate.

Although, as I said before, the eagle is holding its own
in Scotland at the present day, this is entirely due to
the increase of land given over to deer. Were it not for
the 3,000,000 acres of deer forests Scotland possesses, the
eagle would by now have shared the fate of the Osprey
and the Sea Eagle ; for during the earlier part of last century a very large number of Golden Eagles were destroyed.
From March 1831 to March 1834 in Sutherland alone as
many as 171 old birds and 53 eggs and young were taken,
and a little earlier—between 1820 and 1826—295 old birds

and 60 young were killed. A keeper trapped 15 eagles in three months in 1847. The captured birds found a ready market, for about the year 1850 English buyers used to give £5 for an eagle for stuffing. Large as was the number of eagles formerly killed in the Highlands, it does not nearly approach a record from Norway, where, during the five years ending 1850, no less than 10,715 eagles were accounted for.

The Golden Eagle is nowadays protected by law, and few are shot, except when they wander from their forest homes to adjoining grouse moors. In these latter situations the eagle can never be looked upon with favour, although I am sure that the damage ascribed to them is often exaggerated. The range of a pair of eagles during the nesting season is so wide a one that on a well-stocked grouse moor the actual damage done must always be slight. But it must be admitted that many a grouse drive has been entirely spoiled before now by the sudden and unwelcome appearance of an eagle just at the critical moment. I do not think that, at the present time, the eagle is found south of Perthshire to the east, and Argyllshire to the west in this country, but formerly it had a much wider range. In Wales the eagle bred on Snowdon in the seventeenth century. Here it was known as Eryr Melyn—" Yellow Eagle "—and Eryr Euraidd—" Golden Eagle." The Snowdon Hills are, I believe, to this day known as " Creig ian'r Eryri," or The Eagle Rocks. Evans in the *History of Wales* (1880), speaks of the Golden Eagle being found even at this late date about Snowdon. Going back to the sixteenth century, we have evidence of eagles in Denbighshire, and Leland writes of Castell Den : " There bredith on the rock side that the Castelle standith on every year an Egle, and the egle doth sorely assaut him that destroith the nest by going down in one Basket and having another over his hedde to defend the sore stripe of the Egle."

The Lake District was another former home of the
eagle. So long ago as 1272, it was written that the
tenants in Liddesdale must preserve the nests of sparrow-
hawks and eagles. In the seventeenth century they
bred among the mountains of central and western Lake-
land, notably in the region of the precipices at the
head of Ullswater lake. Pennant wrote of the mountains
at the head of Windermere, that eagles breed in many
places. " Those who take their nests find in them great
numbers of moorgame ; they are besides very pernicious to
heronries : it is remarked in the laying season of the herons,
when the eagles terrify them from their nests, that crows,
watching their opportunity, will steal away their eggs."
In 1833 the Golden Eagle bred in Dumfriesshire, while
in Kirkcudbrightshire the last nests were towards the end
of the fifties. In 1668 a Golden Eagle's eyrie was reported from Derbyshire on trustworthy evidence, and
about 1750 it bred on Cheviot, a fine hill 2700 feet in
height in Northumberland. In Ireland it still frequents
some of the most mountainous and least-frequented districts, but is not so common as was formerly the case.
It is said that the Golden Eagles nesting on the Outer
Hebrides are smaller and darker in colour than those of
the mainland. The eggs here are laid during the first
week of April, which is over a fortnight later than on the
mainland.

There is no bird which has so wide a range as the
Golden Eagle—in fact, it is met with almost throughout the world. Considering the numbers of eagles which
leave the nest each year in Scotland, it is surprising
that there should not be a more marked increase in their
numbers, but it is possible the young birds migrate to the
continent, as the North Sea must form a quite ineffectual
barrier to a bird possessing the wing power of the eagle.
With the exception of Iceland, from which, curiously enough,

it is absent, the Golden Eagle breeds from Scandinavia to North Africa. It is common in Spain, where it has a deadly hatred against the Griffon Vulture, and it extends across Europe and North Asia. It is found among the Himalayas and in the Atlas Mountains. In the Himalayas it is confused with the Bearded Vulture, which is sometimes given the name of Golden Eagle. In China it is a resident species, but does not inhabit Greenland, so far as I know. In Lapland it makes its nest in large trees, and this is often the case in Germany also. In Palestine it is common in winter, and occurs sometimes in Arabia and Egypt, and even in Abyssinia. In America it extends as far south as Mexico, though the North American forms are, I believe, rather smaller and darker than the British specimens. In the northern parts of the Schwarzwald the eagle is considered to be a rare visitor, but in March I had an excellent sight of a pair from the summit plateau of the Hornisgrinde, a hill just over 4000 feet high. They crossed over the plateau, sailing and circling in true eagle fashion until they were lost to view towards the valley of the Rhine. As the eagle does not nest hereabouts, I imagine that these two specimens came from the Alps, a hundred miles or so to the southward.

In the Crimea, where many ideal nesting sites exist, the eagle is common. Along the coast of the Black Sea, from Sevastopol to Yalta, are giant cliffs where the eagles are constantly seen. I once observed here as many as seven in the air together while midway between the two towns above mentioned, and after watching them for a time several of the birds sailed up into the clouds and were lost to view. I have seen this same thing happen in Scotland, and have wondered whether the birds can find their bearings without difficulty when making their way through an impenetrable blanket of fog. I imagine that in the Crimea the food supply must be a matter of concern, for on that peninsula there are no birds such as the eagles prey on in these islands. Either, I imagine, the eagles must feed largely on sea-birds or else subsist upon the smaller land songsters, of which there are many in the district. It seemed to me that the Crimean eagles were larger and not quite so graceful in their soaring as our own native birds ; but I had not sufficient time to study them as fully as I should have liked. In Eastern Turkestan, where it lives on the stag, the antelope, the wolf, and the fox, the eagle is trained for falconry, and such a trained bird was valued at the price of two camels.

In this country the Golden Eagle has no wide migration, though it often moves over to grouse moors during severe weather. Scarcely a winter passes without the report of the capture of a Golden Eagle along our east or south-east coasts, but such birds are, in nine cases out of ten, immature Sea Eagles. A friend of mine told me he once saw in the New Forest a bird which seemed to him to be a Golden Eagle—and he has had much experience of the eagle in Scotland. There was a whole gale of wind blowing at the time, and the eagle was only a short distance from the ground. A Golden Eagle was obtained in Lincolnshire on November 1, 1881, and again on October 29, 1895, but there are few authenticated cases of its appearance south of the Tweed during the last half-century. Eagles vary so much in size that accurate measurements are difficult.

As is the case with most birds of prey, the female is the larger and more powerfully built of the two, and a specimen is recorded from Northumberland which measured no less than 11 feet 3 inches from wing tip to wing tip. This is quite out of the ordinary for a British eagle, but recently, when in the forest of Gaick, I saw an eagle which was noticeable as having, even at the height at which it was soaring, a spread of wing of exceptional length. I should say that, on an average, a mature cock eagle has a spread of wing from 6 to 7 feet, and a hen from 7 to 8 feet. The length of the birds varies from $2\frac{1}{2}$ feet to $3\frac{1}{2}$ feet, and the weight from 12 to 14 lbs. These measurements are from a male eagle : Length 32 inches, wing 24·5 inches, tail 13 inches, tarsus 3·7 inches. A female showed a length of 35·5 inches, a wing of 27·5, tail 14 inches, and tarsus 3·8 inches.

The Golden Eagle has the bill horn-coloured or deep blue-black, the tip being the darkest. The iris is of a clear orange brown, the pupil black. The crown of the head and the nape are russet. Chin and throat dark brown. Breast brown, ending in a reddish tint. Back dark brown, the lesser wing coverts being lighter in colour. Primaries nearly black. Secondaries brownish black. Wing coverts brown. Rest of the body brown, and this brown becomes lighter with advancing years. Tail deep brown, paler at the base, and barred irregularly with dark brown. Upper tail coverts pale brown tinged with grey. The legs, which are heavily feathered, are light brown. The feet are yellow. Expanse of foot 7 inches, including the claws. These latter are black, and the outer one is the smallest of the four. During the first year there is a well-defined white bar on the upper half of the tail, but this becomes less with each moult. In *immature* plumage the secondaries are white for three-quarters of their length, and this applies to the tail also. Upper tail coverts white, some tipped with brown, undertail coverts the same. Legs covered with white feathers inside. The plumage is very similar in male and female. When newly hatched, the eaglets have pink eyes, and when plumaged the wing coverts are patched with white. White varieties of the Golden Eagle have been from time to time reported. I believe the following distinction enables immature Golden Eagles to be identified from immature Sea Eagles : The foot of the Golden Eagle has the tarsus clothed and each toe covered with small reticulations as far as the last phalanx. In the foot of the White-tailed Eagle, on the other hand, the reticulations are confined to the tarsus.

I should be reluctant to bring this chapter to an end without putting forward an earnest request to all nature lovers, and to all lovers of the remote hill places, that they should see the Golden Eagle is always afforded protection. He is, without doubt, the finest representative of bird life in these islands, and I am sure that without his dark, inscrutable presence the glens and corries of the hill country would appear lonely and desolate indeed.

2. THE WHITE-TAILED OR SEA EAGLE

IOLAIR BHREAC (Speckled Eagle), IOLAIR BHUIDHE (Yellow Eagle), IOLAIR-BHAIN, IOLAIR CHLADAICH (Shore Eagle), IOLAIR MHARA, IOLAIR RIABHACH (Brindled Eagle). IOLAIR-SÙIL-NA-GRÈINE (*Gaelic*); ORN, ASSA (*Icelandic*); AIGLE À QUEUE BLANCHE (*French*); SEE-ADLER, MEER-ADLER (*German*).

So lately as 1883 no less an authority than Seebohm put it on record that the White-tailed Eagle was a far more common bird than the Golden Eagle in the British Isles. Even though the statement was not too correct, it gives, I think, a fair idea of the rapid decrease of the Sea Eagle within our confines during recent years, for in 1914, when this chapter is being written, there are at most only two pairs of these birds nesting in Britain. As is the case with the Osprey, the Erne—as the Sea Eagle was formerly called—is on the point of extinction. The cause of its rapid decrease may be set down to its partiality for lambs, for it is not, like the Osprey, a migrant in the true sense of the word, and has no dangers to run during the migration north and south like the Fish Hawk. I believe that if its nesting sites had been more remote and inaccessible, as those of the Golden Eagle, it would have held its own. Unlike the latter bird, however, its eyries have been situated almost entirely along the coast-line—on the west of Scotland, where sheep-farming is largely practised—and its fondness for lambs has resulted in traps being laid for it in various ways by irate shepherds and sheep farmers.

An instance may be quoted as showing the merciless destruction of the Ernes. The hen bird was shot near the nest, but the male eagle succeeded in procuring another mate. Soon he himself shared the fate of his first wife, whereupon the second and foster-mother, showing a commendable interest in the eaglets, took her departure and soon reappeared with another male to assist her in her self-imposed task of rearing the family. Her devotion did no more than to cause her own destruction, and the imported male took his departure, abandoning the eyrie and its contents.

There was, it must be admitted, a strong incentive to shoot the eagles quite apart from the damage they caused, for a reward of ten shillings was formerly paid in Skye for each Erne accounted for, and on one occasion no less than three eagles were shot in the course of a single morning whilst gorging on a dead sheep. Is it to be wondered at, then, that the Sea Eagle, formerly so numerous, had ceased to breed on the Isle of Skye by the year 1890 ? In Orkney, too, the eagle was treated as an outcast of the most dangerous type. Here there is, or was, an old custom that anyone killing a White-tailed Eagle should be entitled to a hen from every house situated in the parish in which the bird was killed, while so long ago as 1800 the Commissioners of Supply paid out five shillings for every eagle destroyed. Doubtless, as a result of such incessant and organised persecution, the Sea Eagle ceased to nest in Orkney about the year 1880. About this time, too, it disappeared from Cape Wrath, though on the sea cliffs of Ireland it was said to be not uncommon in 1883, and nested in Mayo till recently. In earlier times the Bass Rock, that well-known landmark from North Berwick, had its pair of Sea Eagles. In 1835 it still nested in the Lake District, and other strongholds were the Isle of Man, the Isle of Wight, and Lundy Island.

In disposition it is much more roving than the Golden Eagle, and scarcely a season passes without some immature specimen, on its migration south, being shot by a sportsman and reported in the local press as a Golden Eagle.

The persecution of the Erne has by no means been confined to the islands. On the mainland, in Western Ross, a single keeper killed no less than fifty-two Sea Eagles during the course of twelve years, and during a winter a hill shepherd accounted for five. Sometimes, however, the birds nested in lofty precipices, where a successful shot was difficult, and where the nest was out of reach. Under such circumstances burning peats were let down to the nest, with hopes that the peat would set fire to the eyrie. I believe this expedient was tried with considerable success, and also that of lowering bundles of cotton wool into a nest containing young eagles. The youngsters, on seeing the white object descending on to them, imagined that an enemy was making an attack, and lay on their backs, striking upwards with their talons, as is the custom with the young of birds of prey when defending themselves. Their claws, during their thrusts, became firmly embedded in the cotton wool, and thus they were drawn up to the surface.

Choosing, as it does, less alpine nesting sites than the Golden Eagle, it is somewhat surprising to find that the Erne is rather later in commencing nesting operations than the latter bird, and it is usually the first week in April before the eggs are laid. The nesting materials are much the same as those utilised by the Golden Eagle, only I believe that freshly-pulled fir branches, which are such a feature of Golden Eagles' eyries, are not found in nests of the white-tailed species. Still, in both cases the plant *Luzula sylvatica* is chosen as a receptacle for the eggs, though the White-tailed Eagle may sometimes add a bunch or two of seaweed for the adornment of the home. The eggs are usually two in number, three are occasionally found, and an instance is on record of four being discovered. When first laid they are of a greyish white colour, quite unspotted, and can thus be at once distinguished from those of the Golden Eagle. In size they average $3\frac{1}{8}$ by $2\frac{3}{8}$ inches.   It is said that, when three eggs are found in an eyrie, one is always unfertile.

In these islands the nesting site of the Sea Eagle has usually been a lofty precipice along the sea coast.   At times the situation chosen was an inland one, however, and in an eyrie sixty miles from the coast a fresh mackerel was found.   Like its relative, the Golden Eagle, the white-tailed species has often two eyries placed a short distance from each other, and these it uses not quite alternately, but as occasion may demand.   The eyrie is a bulky structure, from 6 feet to 8 feet in diameter, and often reaches a great age before it is brought to the ground by a heavy snowfall or a gale of exceptional severity.

Though in the British Isles the Sea Eagle has not been found—at all events within recent times—nesting in trees, it not infrequently chooses such a situation in Germany, where its eyrie has been seen on the Scots fir, oak, and beech.   Curiously enough, a Grey Crow's nest has been taken in the same tree as that containing a Sea Eagle's eyrie.   Even where lofty cliffs abound the Sea Eagle does not always make use of them.   Thus in Shetland, where inaccessible nesting sites are plentiful, an eyrie has actually been found on the ground.

When hatched out, the young of the White-tailed Eagle are clad in down of a considerably darker colour than the fledgelings of the Golden Eagle.   The parent birds, immediately after the hatching of the eaglets, sit more closely than at any other time.   When flushed from her eyrie, the mother Sea Eagle usually sails off in silence, but at times give utterance to sharp yelping cries which are, if anything, more penetrating than those of the Golden Eagle.

From the day they first see the light, the eaglets are supplied with a most liberal allowance of food.   In an eyrie containing two young birds about a week old were found two eider ducks, one hen red-breasted merganser, one hen goosander, and a brace of long-tailed duck. Certainly no stinting of rations. On another occasion close on a dozen cod-fish of various sizes were found in a nest. I believe the grey gurnard is a favourite article of food with this eagle, on account of the habit of these fish of swimming near the surface of the water.

It is generally the first days of August before the young Sea Eagles are able to leave the eyrie. As the nest is frequently placed on high cliffs overlooking the sea, it is thus necessary that the eaglets should be strong on the wing before they make their initial flight. This, the following incident will show. A young Sea Eaglet on making its first flight from the eyrie set out seawards. The parent bird pursued its child, and convinced it of its mistake. The eaglet now endeavoured to regain the land, but its strength was not sufficient to carry it back to safety, and it fell into the water. The parent bird, showing the greatest anxiety, succeeded in picking up the youngster, and even in carrying it a short distance, but before the land had been gained was obliged to drop the unfortunate eaglet, which perished in the waves.

A couple of Sea Eagles, taken from the eyrie when young, once became so tame that they joined their owner on his walks, circling in the air high above him, and even retrieving his game. They were unfortunately shot by a sportsman who imagined they were wild representatives.

The prey of the Sea Eagle consists by no means entirely of fish. On one occasion a specimen was seen in hot pursuit of a grouse. The line of flight of the fugitive took it across a sea loch. Upon reaching the farther shore of the loch, the grouse dropped suddenly to the ground and darted into a hole amongst the rocks, just above the level of the water. The eagle, somewhat at a loss for a plan of action, took up its station on the top of a boulder, hoping that the grouse would in time emerge once more into the open. As quickly as possible the witness of the occurrence hurried to the spot, and found the unfortunate grouse half-drowned in its hole owing to the flow of the tide, seemingly preferring to meet its death in this fashion, rather than to risk an encounter with the eagle.

It was, as I have said, largely owing to its fondness for sheep and lambs, especially the latter, that the Sea Eagle has had every man's hand directed against it along the Western Highlands. It has been seen raising and dropping young lambs merely for sport, just as its relative the Golden Eagle passes its time with grouse and hares, rising with them to a great height, dropping them from its talons, and endeavouring to overtake and recapture them before they reach the ground.

I think that the White-tailed Eagle is a more carrion-eating bird than the Golden Eagle, for whereas the latter bird prefers to hunt its prey, the Sea Eagle seems to find the carcase of a sheep, lying on the hillside, or thrown up by the tide, equally appetising. Its feeding habits, too, are not so cleanly ; even when it has captured a rabbit, it often eats only the viscera, leaving the flesh untouched. It preys, too, on various aquatic birds, such as gulls, puffins, and guillemots, and in a specimen was once found a puffin which had been swallowed whole. Even before the eggs hatch out prey is sometimes brought to the nest —a guillemot and two kittiwakes have been found in an eyrie containing eggs only. Unlike the Golden Eagle it undoubtedly does some of its hunting by night, and its plunge into the sea after some unlucky fish has not infrequently been heard, the great form of the eagle passing swiftly by in the gloom. The propensity of the Sea Eagle for striking at fish of great size has sometimes ended disastrously for the would-be captor. A Sea Eagle once came ashore in Hoy, quite dead, with its feet fast in a fish. Again in the Shetlands a halibut was found with an eagle's feet fast in its back, the bird itself having rotted off. A specimen was also found with its claws fast in a salmon.

A curious tradition exists in the north—a tradition having probably as its origin the fact that an eagle at times strikes at a fish too powerful for it to raise from the surface of the water—to the effect that a Sea Eagle, having despatched its victim, spreads its wings wide, and using them as sails, makes for the shore with its prey. But that the Sea Eagle is capable of lifting great weights is borne out from the fact that a trout of no less than twelve pounds was taken from an eyrie in the Lake District. During spells of frost, when the inland waters are frozen over, the Sea Eagle is said to break the ice—provided the latter is not of too great thickness—by stooping at and through it. Still, should necessity arise, the bird is able to exist without food for long periods, and one has been known to fast for four or five weeks. Such was the hatred of the Highland farmers towards the Sea Eagle that when captured the birds were sometimes thrown alive into some disused barn, and there left to starve slowly to death.

It is not, I think, disputed that the Sea Eagle has a less courageous nature than the King of Birds. One could not imagine a Golden Eagle waiting quietly for an otter to end its repast before finishing off the remnants, but a Sea Eagle was unwilling to come to close quarters till the otter had finished its meal. A pair of skuas have been known to attack and rout a Sea Eagle which had ventured too near their nesting site. A Sea Eagle has been known to attack a sleeping seal, though the result of the encounter is not chronicled, and one has been seen to carry off a pig.

It is probable that, like the Golden Eagle, the White-tailed Eagle pairs for life, so that encounters between two male birds are not frequent. On one occasion, however, two Sea Eagles fought over a loch, and after a time both combatants fell to the water. Whether the bird which struck the water first was dead before its fall cannot be stated definitely; certain it is that the upper of the two birds flew off apparently uninjured, while the lower floated lifeless on the surface of the loch.

The powers of flight, too, of the Sea Eagle are, perhaps, also inferior to those of the Golden Eagle. This fact was noticed by Aristotle, for he observes that the Sea Eagle's flight is weak on account of a shade which crosses the eye. This statement caused Aldrovandus to examine the eye, and he discovered that the portion of the pupil which is commonly covered only with the cornea is in the White-tailed Eagle lined with an exceedingly delicate membrane that has actually the appearance of a small spot.

More fanciful was the statement made by Pliny, to the effect that Sea Eagles breed small vultures, which in their turn engender greater vultures. It is comforting to be told that these latter have not the power of propagation. In more recent times Buffon believed in the mating of the Sea Eagle with the Osprey, though I do not think recent investigations have borne out this belief.

Albino Sea Eagles have been noted from time to time. In 1879 such a White Sea Eagle was seen in the Shetlands. The fact is of interest, for as I write—1914—one of the last remaining representatives in our islands is a white specimen—in all probability the same bird as that noticed thirty-five years ago, for she is now of such a great age that, her last clutch of eggs proving infertile, her mate left her, and she now haunts her former nesting site alone, appearing like a gigantic gull as she takes wing and soars leisurely out over the sea.

Like the Osprey, the Sea Eagle has a wide range throughout Europe. In Iceland it is resident, though not common, and I believe on the decrease. It feeds in that island on trout and char. In South Greenland it is said to be common throughout the year, but to be found in North Greenland only in the summer ; it is also met with nesting in certain localities from the Arctic Circle to the Mediterranean. I was informed while in the Maritime Alps, that the Sea Eagle was found in that district, though it was considerably outnumbered by the Golden Eagle. It is of migratory disposition, and many of the north nesting specimens winter in Southern Europe and North Africa. A few of these birds are said to remain to nest on the Canary Islands, Algeria, and Egypt. In Siberia the White-tailed Eagle breeds south of the Arctic Circle, and on the approach of winter moves down into Persia, Turkestan, and Southern China, occasionally crossing the Himalayas to India. In the Crimea, and eastward from that point, it is replaced by Pallas' Sea Eagle, which has been known to make its nest on a low sandy island of the Black Sea ; and there is a tradition amongst the Tartars that the wounds of its claws are fatal. Along the lower Danube valley the Sea Eagle is numerous, but in Central Russia it is rare.

Description.—Head and upper neck ashy grey, inclining to white with a creamy tinge. Most of the feathers are dull brown at the base. Lower neck, forepart of the back, and wing coverts dull brown, all the feathers being broadly edged or terminated with dirty white, tinged with cream colour. The remainder of the back, rump, and upper tail coverts dark brown, some of the latter being marked or marbled with white ; quills blackish brown, the shafts whitish. Inner secondaries of a somewhat lighter brown, scapulars dark brown. Tail rounded, and pure white except at the base, where the feathers are blackish brown. Under parts brown. Under tail coverts dark brown. Bill pale bluish, becoming yellow at the base. In old birds the beak is almost entirely yellow. Iris, straw coloured; feet, light yellow; claws, bluish black. Total length, just under three feet. In immature birds the tail is darker—in fact, it has been stated that it is not until the eagle has reached the age of six years that the tail becomes fully white. As is the case with the Golden Eagle, the female bird is the larger, but closely resembles her mate in the matter of plumage. As compared with the Golden Eagle, the Sea Eagle has the tail shorter, the wings broader and more rounded.

Since writing this chapter I hear that a pair of White-tailed Eagles are still occasionally seen in a certain district of Skye, which must be nameless, and my informant has little doubt that they breed on some high cliffs near the site of an ancient eyrie.

On the lonely island of St. Kilda the Sea Eagle sometimes makes her nest, but here the birds are not looked on with favour by the inhabitants. The people of St. Kilda endeavour to set fire to their nests or to frighten the birds away, since their presence disturbs the valuable Fulmar Petrel.

THE OSPREY

PANDION HALIÆTUS

Iasgair (The Fisher), Iolair-iasgaich, Iolair-iasgair (*Gaelic*); Skopa (*Russian*); formerly known in Burgundy as Crau pêcherot, or Crow Fisher.

To give an account of the history of the Osprey in these islands is to chronicle a succession of regrettable events —events which are responsible for the loss to us of a noble bird, that in former days added a great charm to many a lonely loch hidden away amongst the Scottish hills. To say the Osprey is extinct with us would not be quite correct, since one or two birds are seen every year in various parts of the country during the spring and autumn migration, and there are rumours even now that a pair renew their eyrie and rear their family in an unfrequented spot along the west coast of Scotland. But the unfortunate fact remains that through our want of protection, Iolair an uisge (the Eagle of the Water) as the Osprey is known to the Gael, must now, to all intents and purposes, be counted among our lost birds. Not so many years ago there was scarcely a loch in Scotland but had its pair of Fishing Eagles. On Loch Maree was formerly an eyrie, and Loch Awe, in the Campbell country, harboured at least one pair. To Loch Tay, that famous sheet of water, containing early spring salmon in their thousands, the Osprey made his way each year with the coming of the warm season, and Loch Lomond, I believe, sheltered another pair. On Loch an Eilan, under the shadow of Cairngorm, and on Loch Arkaig, in the country of the west coast and of Ben Nevis, the Osprey lingered till only a few years ago, but now has ceased to frequent even these ancient strongholds. It is no exaggeration to say that it is owing to two factors, and to two factors alone, that the Fishing Eagle has failed to hold its own within our confines. These factors are, the migratory instinct of the birds, and the large remuneration given by mis-guided collectors for British-taken eggs of the Osprey. Neither cause, I think, would of itself have been sufficient to banish the Osprey, but against the two combined it has had little chance of struggling successfully.

After the close of the nesting season, and on the approach of the cold weather, the Osprey is in the habit of leaving its native loch and making its way south. A supply of food in northern waters is no doubt difficult to procure during the winter months, for the trout and other fish seek the depths of the lochs, where the Osprey cannot penetrate. Besides this, the Fishing Eagle is a comparatively thin-skinned bird, and is thus less fitted to withstand the cold than its second cousin, the Golden Eagle. The Eagle makes its home among the hills and glens summer and winter, and is still common enough if one knows the corries to search ; the Osprey forsakes the shelter of the hills, and is on the point of extinction.

Some years ago a pair of Ospreys were shot on the river Avon in Hampshire. The birds were on migration at the time, and were probably making their way from some Scottish loch to their southern winter quarters. It is possible that they were the pair from far-distant Loch an Eilan—at all events, the loch is nowadays deserted. On Loch an Eilan the Osprey had its eyrie in earlier times on the ruined castle still bidding defiance to the storms and situated on a small island not more than a hundred yards from the mainland. I did not, unfortu-nately, know the loch when it gave the Ospreys their nesting site, but their former home may still be made out from the mainland, though the winds from the high hills have partially demolished the nest, except the foundations, which still remain. It was on a wild January day that a friend and I rowed over to the castle and inspected the disused eyrie. The nest was composed of sticks of various sizes, and from what I could see must, in the days of its use, have closely resembled a Golden Eagle's eyrie. It had evidently been a structure of considerable size, and, indeed, one which was weighed turned the scale at four hundred pounds !

From her nest the Osprey had one of Scotland's finest views. At the time of our visit a sou'-westerly gale had removed the snow from the lower grounds, but on Cairngorm to the east it still lay deep, covering the higher slopes of the hill with an unbroken mantle. On the summit the force of the gale was such that snow was being drifted across the hill-top in dense clouds, though lower down the " fresh " of the earlier part of the day followed by frost had formed an icy cake to the snow, preventing the wind from scattering the particles before it. Across the loch white-tipped waves were being hurried, and in the pines fringing the water the wind was passing with that characteristic sound—as the breaking of surf upon a distant shore. One could not but feel a sense of regret that the birds of prey had been banished—it is to be feared for ever—from their loch.

Year after year, before April was many days old, the Ospreys used to arrive at Loch an Eilan, untired after their long journey from the far-distant Mediterranean, where they had spent the winter in summer sunshine, fishing in a sea of deep azure blue. For long the Ospreys held their own, and a pair, probably their children, constructed a nest in a Scots fir on the shore of Loch Mhorlich, the tree being, I believe, known as Craobh na h'Iolaire (the Eagle's Tree).

Misfortunes, however, were not long in overtaking them. There has always been a certain class of egg-collectors which does not seem to rest content until it has secured a clutch of eggs of all our most rare British birds, and it is largely owing to these people that the Osprey is on the verge of extinction. The Loch an Eilan Ospreys had a considerable amount of protection afforded them, but unless a night watcher had been stationed on the mainland opposite the nesting site, it would have been impossible to have protected the eggs at all efficiently. There was a certain daring individual who swam across to the island one dark night, when six inches of snow covered the ground. Clambering with difficulty up the snow-covered ruins, he secured the two eggs which the nest contained. But he now discovered that his cap, in which he had intended to carry back his treasures, had been left on the bank, and the water, with its temperature near freezing-point, was too cold to allow of a second journey. He thereupon took an egg in each hand, and using his legs only to keep him afloat, he was dragged back by an accomplice by means of a rope he had carried over on his outward swim. Half-way back he was seized with cramp but was pulled safely ashore after what, it must be confessed, was an act requiring no little courage. On another occasion the same man made a successful raid, and besides securing the eggs, nearly succeeded in capturing the mother bird, for his hand touched her before she realised his proximity, and flew screaming from the nest.

It is said that the Osprey will lay a second time provided she has sat only a day or two on her eggs, but as many of the clutches taken have contained quite well-grown young, it is certain that these pairs made no attempt at rearing a second family. In a recent work by a well-known Scottish naturalist, the suggestion is advanced that we should follow the example of our cousins in America and should erect, in the shallow waters of our lochs, posts with cart wheels fastened to their summits. These cart wheels are approximately the same size as an Osprey's eyrie, and are intended to catch the eye of any wandering Osprey on the lookout for a nesting site. The idea is a sound one, and might well be put into practice by some of our landowners having suitable lochs on their estates ; but so few Ospreys visit these islands during the spring migration north that I am very doubtful if even a single pair could be induced to nest. To begin with, I am informed that there are now scarcely any Scandinavian Ospreys left, and, indeed, if a pair did by chance decide to nest in this country, they would in all probability chose Loch an Eilan or Loch Arkaig as their quarters. It is only during the last few years that the Loch Arkaig eyrie has been deserted. Quite a decade has elapsed since the last young were raised, but after this a solitary Osprey put in an appearance on the loch each spring for a period of, I believe, seven years. It seemed as though this bird was unable to secure a mate, though it is difficult to imagine that this could have been so, for the Osprey is quite a well-known bird along the Mediterranean seaboard during the winter months, and if the Loch Arkaig Osprey made its winter quarters there, as is probable, it must have met with a number of its fellows. But with the Loch an Eilan Ospreys, too, the same thing happened ; a solitary bird appeared for a time before the nesting site became entirely deserted, so that the difficulty of securing a mate must be considerable, unless, indeed, these individuals were barren birds past the period of nesting, which is hardly likely.

The eyrie on Loch Arkaig is built on a stunted oak tree on a small island, where the birds were comparatively secure during the nesting season. But, unfortunately, this protection could not be afforded them after they left their West Highland loch on their migration southward, and they probably fell victims to a gunner in the course of their winter wanderings, or on their arrival in Southern England with the coming of another spring.

The Osprey has sometimes been given the name of Mullet Hawk, and in the case of the pair above mentioned such a designation would appear singularly appropriate, for though in Loch Arkaig—a fresh-water loch—there are many fish, yet the Ospreys did almost all their hunting on Loch Eil and Loch Linnhe, land-locked fjords of the broad Atlantic, and the fish with which they winged their way back to the home loch was, nine times out of ten, a mullet. When on a fishing expedition the Osprey flies some distance—from a hundred to two hundred feet—above the water, and on sighting its intended prey immediately checks its flight, hovering like a great Kestrel as it decides whether or not the prospective victim is sufficiently near the surface to justify a plunge. The Osprey does not dive ; it makes the attack with feet stretched out to their full, and so rapid is the stoop that the fish seldom has sufficient time to move down to deeper water before the bird of prey is upon it and, grasping it firmly with one talon, gives itself one or two shakes to drive the water from its feathers, and then soars away to its eyrie.

In olden days, before naturalists were familiar with its habits, the Osprey was said to swim with one foot and to catch fish with the other—a quaint statement and very far from the truth. To enable it to cope successfully with such elusive animals as fish in their native element the claws of the Fish Eagle are somewhat modified ; while in other hawks the claws are flat beneath and edged, they are rounded in the Osprey, so as not to tear the fish and to enable them to be more easily withdrawn. This precaution is necessary, for at times the Osprey will grapple with a fish so powerful and heavy that the captor is quite unable to raise it from the water, and cases are on record of the birds being dragged by their prey beneath the surface. This can happen but rarely, however, for the Osprey, although itself weighing only four or five pounds, is able to lift a fish of considerably greater weight than itself. Such a fish taken by the Osprey and partly eaten when found weighed no less than six pounds. The method in which the Osprey carries its prey is interesting : in order to reduce wind resistance to a minimum the Fishing Eagle carries the fish with the head pointing in the direction of its flight, and a bird has been known to turn a fish round in mid-air so as to bring its head to the front. During the flight both feet are used for holding the prey, but immediately before alighting one foot is disengaged and stretched forward to grasp the perch. The other talon, holding the fish, also grips the branch, though less securely, and the fish is held firm by the weight of the bird.

The Osprey is quite six weeks later than the Golden Eagle in commencing the duties of rearing a family, and the eggs are not often laid before the advent of May. They are two or three in number, though on one occasion as many as seven were found in a single eyrie, and are marked most handsomely with rich red-brown spots and blotches. They are perhaps the most beautiful of any eggs laid by a British bird, and, indeed, it may have been partly owing to this that collectors were induced to offer such large reward for their acquisition. In size they naturally vary somewhat, but a normal measurement is, according to Dresser, $2\frac{16}{40}$ by $1\frac{31}{40}$ inches.

The Osprey is a fairly close sitter, and shows a considerable amount of courage where the defence of her eggs or young is concerned. It is on record that the angry parent swooped at a boy who was climbing a tree with the intention of taking the eggs, and fixed her talons in his cap, carrying it off triumphantly. The boy was so unnerved by this episode that, it is good to relate, he abandoned his attempt on the eyrie and was thankful to get to the ground in safety. It is curious and interesting how often the ruins of some ancient castle are chosen as the site for an eyrie, and a nest has even been found built upon the remains of a disused shooting lodge.

The period of incubation is said to be four weeks, though I am inclined to suspect that the eggs are brooded upon for more than thirty days before the young are hatched. These are at first clad in a coat of down, darker considerably than that worn by a baby Golden Eagle, and, like the latter, are provided with a small knob on the upper mandible to enable them the more easily to cut their way through the imprisoning shell when the day comes for their arrival into the wide world. It is stated in books of the eighteenth century that the mother Osprey puts her young through a truly Spartan test soon after they are born. She compels them to look straight at the sun, and the one which first weeps during this formidable ordeal is ruthlessly killed and thrown from the eyrie. This noteworthy statement was made, in all probability, to account for the disappearance of one of the young birds at an early age. The quaint theory above mentioned is, as far as I know, without foundation, but all the same this disappearance of one chick from the nest of a bird of prey is a fact for which no really satisfactory explanation has yet been given. The young Ospreys, which are hatched with open eyes, are fed entirely on fish; and when they are in their younger stages the parent bird is careful to give them only small and tender morsels, torn off with her bill. Mullet is the favourite article of food, but where this is not procurable, pike, carp, grilse, and trout are taken; and an Osprey is recorded as having captured an eel two feet long. The Osprey seems to strike well towards the head of the fish, in other words, " it aims well forward," and I believe the head of the victim is often torn clean off by the impact of the stoop.

The young are hatched during the first days of June in this country and are ready to leave the eyrie by the end of July. For some little time after this date they remain in their northern haunts, and are taught the art of capturing fish for themselves, but leave for the south before winter has made herself felt amongst the high-lying glens. I hear from Mr. Meade Waldo that a young Osprey—whether hatched on these islands is doubtful—spent three weeks in a Yorkshire district in September 1912. It became so tame that it was possible to approach and even to stand under the tree in which it was perched. Wood-pigeons and Stock-doves settled fearlessly by it, and, as far as is known, it continued its southern migration un-scathed. This bird may possibly have been hatched from a certain Scottish eyrie where it is said that the birds still nest in security, and it would be interesting to learn whether it eluded its enemies and was able to return in the spring. As far as I am aware, it has never been accurately decided at what age the Osprey commen-ces to breed, but it is doubtful whether it starts house-keeping on its own the season after it is born.

If ever the Fishing Eagle should decide to return to us, there are several nesting sites in Scotland where its appearance would undoubtedly be much welcomed. In Ross and Sutherland the Osprey was a well-known bird not so many years ago, and I believe there is in these counties at least one loch known as Loch an Iasgair, which signifies in the Gaelic tongue, Loch of the Fish Eagle or Osprey. To two men, both of them well-known ornithologists, must be put down the wholesale destruc-tion of the Ospreys and their eggs which took place about the middle of the nineteenth century. They were both nature lovers—in a way, but they unfortunately wished to have tangible tokens of the nesting of the Ospreys. One directed his attentions mainly against the birds themselves, while the other—more humanely perhaps—contented himself with removing the clutches of eggs from all those birds which he found nesting. It is easy to make rare, or to exterminate, a bird, but it is most difficult to induce it to take up once more its nesting quarters on these islands. Whether the Osprey will ever re-establish itself successfully remains to be seen. There is no doubt that interest in our rarer birds has increased considerably during recent years. But I have grave doubts whether such interest can save the Osprey from sharing the same fate as the Kite in Scotland. Thirty or forty years ago the Kite was comparatively common in well-wooded districts, now it is quite extinct north of the Tweed. The Osprey is not yet extinct, though hovering on the border-line, and so it behoves all those who are interested in preserving to us the rarer birds of the country to do their utmost to offer strict, the most strict, protection to the Fish Hawk at all times, when or wherever it may be seen.

It might possibly be of use to replace the eggs of a Golden Eagle nesting near the former nesting haunt of the Osprey with the eggs of this latter bird. But the procuring of such eggs would be a matter of great difficulty, and it is extremely doubtful whether the Eagle's diet would agree with the young Ospreys, even though these were successfully hatched out. It is not impossible, however, that the Osprey may again establish itself with us. Its range is a wide one. It is met with, in suitable localities, through the whole of Europe and Africa, and also inhabits Asia, Australia, New Zealand, and the islands of the Pacific. In the south-west of France it appears as a bird of passage, and in April 1914 I saw what I took to be a pair of Ospreys hawking above a river in the neighbourhood of Pau. In America, where it is gregarious, as many as three hundred pairs have been seen nesting on one small island, and it is found as far south as Brazil. It is in America that an amusing story is related of the Osprey. It is said to utter a particular call note when carrying back fish to its young. The Bald-headed Eagle knows this note well, and on hearing it immediately gives chase, usually depriving the captor of its prey. After a time, however, the Ospreys of a certain district, having been robbed of their fish times without number by the Eagle, hit upon an idea of paying out their hereditary enemy. Having stealthily eaten the fish, they flew out over the loch uttering the well-known cry, but carrying only the skeleton of the fish with them. The Eagle, on hearing the note so welcome to him, gave chase immediately, and after doubling and diving for a time the Osprey, to the Eagle's disgust, dropped—not a fish for the gratification of the appetite of the larger bird of prey, but only the backbone, without flesh !

It would appear that the Osprey was formerly used in Great Britain for the capturing of salmon. At all events, by an Act passed in the reign of William and Mary, persons were prohibited at a certain period of the year from taking salmon by Hawks. Evidently the Hawk thus employed was either an Osprey or a Sea Eagle, and it is well known that the former bird is capable of carrying off a good-sized grilse, or even a small salmon, for the gratification of its young.

An abbreviated description of the Osprey may be of interest. There is, I believe, no seasonal change of plumage. The adult male has the head white, striped with dark brown ; ear coverts and a stripe to the hind neck, blackish brown. Upper parts dark glossy brown.

Under parts white, with brown markings on the breast. Legs and cere blue. Iris yellow. Total length about 23 inches, wing 19¼ inches, tail 8¾ inches.

The wing spread is 5 to 6 feet, but Buffon, writing towards the close of the eighteenth century, states explicitly that he has records of an Osprey with a wing expanse of no less than 7 feet 6 inches. If correct, this measurement must have been taken from a quite exceptional bird.

The female in her plumage resembles the male, but she is larger.

It may be of interest to conclude this history of the Iolair an Uisge with us, by the narration of a desperate fight between two birds, near an ancient nesting site in the Scottish Highlands. The origin of the battle is not known—probably two male birds were fighting for a solitary hen—but for two full hours the combatants struggled fiercely above the surface of the loch. At length, however, one of the fighters gained an advantage. He fell to the surface of the water with his rival underneath him, and succeeded in holding the vanquished bird under until it was drowned.

THE PEREGRINE FALCON

FALCO PEREGRINUS

Seabhag, Seabhag bhoirionn seilge, Seabhag-ghorm (*Gaelic*);
Faucon pèlerin (*French*); Wander Falke (*German*); Sapsan
(*Russian*). Local name, Blue Hawk.

Except towards the western seaboard of Scotland, the
Peregrine Falcon is everywhere holding its own with
difficulty, for wherever there is grouse-preserving, there
the Falcon is an outcast and without peace. Every
keeper's hand is against it, and fortunate indeed is that
Peregrine which succeeds in hatching its eggs and rearing
its young in safety.

The persecution of the Peregrine Falcon is, I venture
to suggest, a misguided and unfortunate policy, and can
never be justified when only a single pair of the birds are
nesting on a moor. In very few districts, indeed, is the
Peregrine sufficiently numerous to justify its destruction,
and by an irony of fate it is in these very districts that its
nesting site is so inaccessible that it is next to impossible
to waylay the parents or their brood. In putting forward
an appeal for the protection of the Peregrine Falcon, I
fully realise that the birds do certainly capture a number
of Grouse, and strike down a victim even for the mere
pleasure of killing. But there can also, I think, be little
doubt that the supposed damage is considerably greater
than that actually worked. Personally, I have never yet
seen a Grouse at a Peregrine's eyrie, though I am ready to
admit that my experience is in this respect an exceptional
one. But still I venture to suggest that there are other
birds which form more frequent prey to the Seabhag.

The Grouse, when hard pressed by the Falcon, and realising that its strength is near exhausted, throws itself into any long heather which happens to be near, and crouches motionless in its place of concealment. A Peregrine will rarely take its prey on the ground, and after " waiting on " for a time, in the hopes that its intended victim may rise, the Falcon moves off in search of fresh objects for pursuit.

The two favourite birds of the Peregrine are, perhaps, the Golden Plover and the members of the Duck family. At one eyrie I saw the remains of two Teal Duck and a Golden Plover, evidently killed only a very short time before. In the case of the Plover the head had been severed from the victim's body. At the same nest later on in the season I found the remains of a Coot. The nest was quite two hundred feet above the level of the loch, and as the Coot was in all probability close to the surface when captured, it says a good deal for the lifting power of the Peregrine that it was able to rise with its prey to the top of the rock. It is said that a Coot when captured is carried by its head, as affording the most favourable grip. As showing the partiality of the Peregrine for the Coot, I may mention that an instance is on record of six of these birds being killed by the Falcon in the course of a single day. On one occasion the wing of a Kestrel was found in the eyrie. Pigeons are also captured by the Peregrine, and one has been known to take a Starling after no fewer than eight stoops. I have seen the remains of a Lapwing in the nest, and small birds too mutilated to permit of identification. In former times the Peregrine nested on May Island—an island situated at the entrance to the Firth of Forth and ten miles out from the Bass Rock, and even here a Grouse was found at the nest. The nearest grouse ground to the Island of May is to be found on the distant Lammermoors or Pentlands—or perhaps on the Ochill Hills in Fife—but to a bird which can make its way through the air at a speed of well over a mile a minute, a journey of thirty or forty miles is little thought of. Black Grouse were taken by a pair of Peregrines to their nest on the Bass Rock, though a Black-cock is fully the equal of a Falcon in weight. As an instance of the wing power of the Peregrine, one of these birds belonging to Henry IV of France escaped from its confinement at Fontainebleau, and was found twenty-four hours later in Malta, 1350 miles away. As it is unlikely that the Falcon was noted immediately on its arrival, its speed must have been prodigious, even allowing for winds in its favour, and probably averaged over seventy miles an hour.

The Peregrine Falcon is an early nester among birds of prey in this country—second only to the Golden Eagle—and the Falcon may be brooding by April 10th. The nesting site usually chosen is a rocky hill face, such a hill face with a loch lying beneath being specially favoured, and the nest is on a ledge or cavity of rock. MacGillivray stated in his classical work of the nineteenth century that the nest was a bulky structure, a statement which is difficult of explanation coming from so great an authority, for as far as my experience goes, the Peregrine makes no nest at all, but merely scrapes out a shallow hollow on the ledge and here deposits its eggs. As the same nest is sometimes used year after year, the hollow in time becomes lined with the bones of many bird victims, but this is the only " nest " that one finds. Sometimes the Peregrine may take possession of a Raven's nest for the rearing of the brood, but not without a battle, for the Raven is perhaps the one bird which does not hesitate to show fight where the Falcon is concerned. The eggs usually number three or four, but on one occasion I found five in an eyrie. They are extremely handsome, rich red blotches being distributed lavishly over a ground colour of brown. The duties of incubation are undertaken by

E

the hen bird, who sometimes sits very closely until perhaps she has been rendered wild and unapproachable by persecution. Indeed, I knew of a case in which a stalker succeeded in catching the Falcon as she brooded her eggs. When disturbed she flies out from her nesting ledge in a state of intense excitement and anxiety, moving restlessly backwards and forwards across her nesting site, and uttering her powerful screeching alarm call as she does so. This call soon brings her mate to her side, though he does not usually venture so near the danger zone as does his better half. His cries are uttered more rapidly than those of the Falcon, and are in a higher key. Sometimes on such occasions the form of another male Peregrine is noted, circling at a great height in the sky, and this " hanger on " is probably ready to fill the place of the husband should any mischance happen to him.

For many years now a pair of Peregrines have unsuccessfully attempted to rear their young on a wild rock standing on the summit of a hill two thousand feet in height. The nesting site is an ideal one, but unluckily it is in the heart of the country of the Red Grouse, and thus the Peregrine is looked upon with scant favour. Mountaineers also ascend the hill and frequently prevent the Falcon from returning to her nest for long periods. But still, despite repeated misfortunes, the birds return to their nesting site with every spring, though I doubt whether they have succeeded in rearing a single family during the last decade.

At the present day, when every living thing at all inimical to the Red Grouse is ruthlessly put out of the way, the Balance of Nature must needs be destroyed, and from that fact alone evils must of necessity come. Moors become over-stocked, a trying winter and spring is experienced, and grouse disease makes its appearance. At times such as these the presence of a pair—even of several pairs—of Peregrines on a moor is of undoubted benefit.

THE PEREGRINE FALCON'S HOME.

A Grouse in the early stages of disease offers a more easy mark than such a bird in the full vigour of health, and as a result will, in all probability, be captured. But where no birds of prey are present, where the Eagle and the Peregrine Falcon are considered as vermin and are exterminated so far as is possible, the ravages of the disease continue unchecked, and the moor is decimated in a short space of time.

In the High North, where game-preserving is not, and where are wild tracts of thinly-populated country, the Peregrine Falcon nests on the ground at times. A remarkable and well-authenticated instance of the affection a Peregrine retains for its nesting site comes from Lapland, where the same pair of birds, or their descendants, reared their young on the same hillside for a period of well over a hundred years ; and there are certainly, even in this country, nesting stations which have been occupied for the last fifty years without a break.

The young Peregrines are hatched out about May 15th. At the time of their birth they resemble the young of the Golden Eagle, except for their smaller size, for they are entirely clad in a coat of white down. Compared to the young eagles, their rate of growth is rapid, and before the end of June most of the broods have left the eyrie. For some little time they haunt their nesting site, and even when they are strong on the wing their parents still manifest great solicitude on their behalf, calling restlessly when danger approaches.

The flight of the Peregrine is one of the most splendid things in all the bird world. It might be compared with that of the Eagle as a battleship with the fleetest torpedo destroyer. The Eagle has the majesty which the Peregrine can never hope to possess—for the Falcon has not the weight of the King of Birds—but the Peregrine is the fleeter of the two, and its prey falls to it with greater ease. In the gale the Eagle uses his weight with advantage to enable him to forge ahead through the storm ; the Peregrine relies rather on the powerful thrusts of his clean-cut wings. When pursuing his prey in grim earnest, a Peregrine in good training has been reckoned to fly at the rate of no less than 150 miles an hour, a speed which the Eagle could not attain to unless she was aided by a following wind of great strength. A Golden Plover is also a bird with considerable powers of flight, and as it is able to swerve and twist in the most perplexing manner, it never yields up its life to the Peregrine until after a stern bid for freedom. On one occasion a Peregrine chased a Golden Plover for ten minutes at top speed. At the end of that period the unlucky Plover was exhausted by its efforts and was taken in mid-air. The Plover tribe do not, I think, realise that their best hope of safety lies in their precipitating themselves into the heather like the Grouse, for they continue to rely on their wing power to enable them to escape until they are exhausted. The most striking feature of the Peregrine's flight is its " stooping " powers. Such " stoops " or rushes earthward are not made use of only when the object is to capture prey : they are carried out for the mere joy of flight, and even when their nesting site is visited and their eggs or young are in danger, both Peregrines may be seen periodically to mount up into the sky and then shoot down with tightly-closed wings at terrific speed. When the male and female Peregrines are thus seen together, the superiority in the size of the Falcon is well marked. The weight of the male is about two pounds, while that of the female reaches three—a striking difference. . . . Considering the comparative scarcity of the species in this country, the ease and rapidity with which a survivor finds a new mate, when the latter had been shot, is quite noteworthy. It has been suggested that the survivor makes its way across the North Sea and produces a mate from the Continent ; and, indeed, for a bird with such fine powers of flight this performance would be by no means impossible.

On the west coast of Scotland and, to a lesser extent, on the eastern seaboard, the Peregrine makes its home on the great sea cliffs. Here it preys largely on the inoffensive Puffin, striking down its victims by a stroke from its hind claw and sometimes knocking the head clean off the body.

It is instructive to visit the home of the Peregrine during a season of strong winds and to compare his flight under these weather conditions with that of the Eagle. The Eagle is able to soar up into the breeze with never a movement of his wings till he has disappeared from view. The Peregrine mounts also into the arms of the wind, but in its case repeated movements of its powerful wings are necessary to enable it to reach a great altitude.

After the nesting season the Peregrine wanders far. It is met with along our eastern coast-line, and frequents Holy Island, being attracted by the numbers of duck which have their winter quarters hereabouts. During September 1913 a Peregrine took up its quarters on the Bass Rock, and on more than one occasion I saw it perched on a rock near the summit. From its confiding behaviour I imagine that it had come from the far north, where the Falcon is not subjected to persecution as in these islands.

The range of the Peregrine Falcon is a world-wide one, for it is found through the vast area stretching from Greenland to South Africa. Through the whole of Asia it is met with also, down to Java and Sumatra ; and in the Nearctic region, from Hudson Bay down to the Argentine. Curiously enough, it is absent from Iceland, where perhaps its place is taken by the Iceland Falcon. In India, as in this country, the Peregrine is used for hawking, and among the Hindus its name is Bhyri. To the Persians it is known as Basi.

During their migration many Peregrines are captured for falconry. A light-coloured pigeon is tied to the ground beneath a small bow net, so arranged as to be drawn over quickly by a long string attached to it. This string stretches to a turf shelter, where the falconer is concealed.

Near the "shelter" a Butcher Bird is tied, and two pieces of turf are set up so as to serve him as a retreat. Should a Peregrine appear, even at a great distance, the Butcher Bird utters piercing cries, and the Peregrine, attracted to the spot by his shrieks, marks the pigeon, stoops down, and, if all goes well, is secured in the net. From very early times the sport of falconry has been practised in this country. It was reckoned that a Falcon (the hen Peregrine) was a match for a Heron, or for a Wild Goose, while the Tiercel or male was more suited for Partridges and smaller game. As showing the high prices given for the Peregrine, it is chronicled that in the reign of James II no less than £1000 was given for a pair of these birds. In terms of falconry young Peregrines are known as Red Hawks, adult birds as Haggards. Eyess is another term for the Peregrine.

Description.—In the male the crown, nape, hind neck, and side of head to below the eye are black. Back, scapulars, wing coverts, and secondaries dark slate blue with very dark slate bars traversing them. Lower part of the back considerably lighter in colour, becoming slate blue on the rump and upper tail coverts, which have also darker crossbars. Primaries almost black, on terminal part edged with white. Tail blackish, with broad bars of slate blue at the base. Extreme tip of tail brownish white. Under parts white, with a tinge of warm rufous. Throat and upper breast with a few long markings. Rest of under parts boldly barred with black. Cere and legs yellow. Iris brown. Bill dark bluish horn colour, at base of a light blue. Total length about 16 inches. Wing 12 inches. The female is considerably larger than the male, but in her plumage resembles him.

THE KESTREL

FALCO TINNUNCULUS

Seabhag fhiorinn (*Gaelic*), also Clamhan ruadh ; Faucon cresserelle (*French*) ; Thurm Falke (*German*).

THE Kestrel is the falcon most commonly met with in the moorland districts of the Highlands, and would appear to be holding its own despite the fact that large numbers are shot every year on the Scottish grouse moors.

Ornithologists, indeed all nature lovers, have always been inclined to look upon the destruction of the Kestrel as wanton and unjust. Keepers, on the other hand, have been bitter against it in that it destroyed numbers of the young of game birds, such as Grouse or Partridges. There is a good deal to be said for either side of the question, but of this there is no doubt ; the Kestrel—or Windhover, as it is sometimes called—has a very largely-developed useful side to its character, for its favourite prey consists of mice, which do so much harm to agriculture in these islands. It has been estimated that a single Kestrel, remaining in a district for 210 days, would be the means of destroying no less than 10,395 mice. Indeed, it appears to delay its nesting season according as to whether field mice and insects are plentiful or the reverse. In the Scottish glens the nesting site of the Kestrel is a rocky gorge, through which there often flows a hill burn. That the Kestrel does not strike terror into the hearts of the smaller birds is evident from the fact that several pairs of Ring Ousels are almost invariably to be found nesting near the Red Hawk, with, as like as not, a pair of Dippers, several pairs of Wrens, and maybe a Goosander or Red-breasted Merganser. In one such gorge that I know, a Merlin and a Kestrel nested within a few yards of each other.

In the usual sense of the word, the Kestrel makes no nest. She scrapes a small depression on some rocky ledge, and in this deposits her eggs. She is—after the manner of all falcons—constantly throwing up castings, consisting of the undigested portions and fur of the mice which enter so largely into her diet, and in time these castings form a soft bed of fur on which the eggs repose. The eggs of the Kestrel number from three to five, the latter number being the more usual of the two. In colour, if not in shape, they closely resemble those of the Red Grouse. Over a ground colour of pale reddish white are laid many confused markings of dull brownish red. The eggs lack the pyriform shape common to those of the family of Waders, and at times are almost circular. They are laid towards the end of May, but as early as the opening days of that month the Kestrels may be seen circling and toying with each other above the ground they have chosen as a nesting site. The hen bird is rarely a close sitter, flying out from her nest and circling round the intruder with loud screams. Sometimes, however, she can be approached unawares and even caught as she broods her eggs. It is unusual for more than one pair of Kestrels to tenant the same gorge, but I once knew of two nesting close together, in a place where it was evident a Golden Eagle came frequently to roost. I have seen a Kestrel flying restlessly round her nesting site, pursued with considerable heat by a Ring Ouzel, which was evidently engaged in rearing a brood in the same locality.

The young Kestrels when first hatched are covered with grey white down and grow rapidly. Their food consists mainly of mice—*Mus sylvaticus*, *Mus domesticus*, *Arvicola agrestis*, and shrews, especially *Sorex araneus*.

On one occasion I had a family of young Kestrels under observation for several weeks. On June 18th the young brood were five in number. They were still down-clad, and only the rudiments of a few of their feathers were appearing. On June 29th, when next I visited them, they had matured in quite a noteworthy manner. This time the nest contained only three birds—the remaining two may possibly have succumbed through lack of food—and they were almost ready for flight. It was impossible to obtain satisfactory photographs of them on their nesting ledge, and so, not without difficulty, I succeeded in carrying them up to the top of the rock. The nesting ledge was near the summit of the cliff, and by leaning out on an overhanging birch tree it was possible just to touch the young. As they struck out fiercely with their talons, it was not easy to lift them from the nest, but I succeeded in accomplishing this by enveloping them in the focussing cloth of my camera. The chicks shrieked loudly and repeatedly during this process, and the parent bird, perched in a neighbouring birch, joined in their cries. I placed the trio on a ledge of rock, and they remained obligingly quiet during the time that I secured a number of photographs of them. One of the young birds—a hen, I think—showed less spirit than the other two, and remained during most of the time with her head hidden beneath the wing of one of her companions, who glared fiercely at the hated camera and the still more hated operator ! At no time did I see the remains of any prey in the nest.

It is surprising what uncertainty exists amongst the Highlanders as to the identity of the Kestrel. I have heard it referred to by intelligent stalkers as the Peregrine Falcon, and on one occasion I was asked to call and see what was supposed to be a young Golden Eagle—in reality a youthful and depressed Kestrel

not yet able to fly! . . . To many who watch the
Kestrel as he hovers above a hillside, stooping to earth
every few minutes and rising, apparently with empty
talons, it is surmised that such " stoops " have been unsuccessful.   In reality the Kestrel has been preying on
beetles, and though the rush to earth may have been rewarded by the capture of one of these insects, there is no
visible sign, for the Windhover has devoured his small
prey as quickly as caught.   When hunting, the Kestrel
is rarely more than fifty feet above the moor.   If it has
suspicions that a suitable prey is somewhere on the ground
near it drops a little, then hovers a little, drops again a few
yards, scanning the ground intently, then either dashes
down at top speed—its suspicions confirmed—or else rises
in disgust and flies off to search another part of the hill.

When hovering, a Kestrel faces the wind, spreads its tail
wide, and with the extremities of its wings rapidly vibrating, remains motionless, keenly surveying the ground
beneath.   On sighting its prey it closes its wings and tail,
dropping like a stone till just above the surface of the
ground.

The Kestrel is said to feed on lizards, and is not above
bearing off the young of Grouse, Partridges, and Pheasants,
but still cannot be said to be a murderer and a tyrant
like the Sparrow Hawk.   Mice are sometimes swallowed
entire.   Several instances of a Kestrel " catching a
Tartar " are recorded.   Once a bird, after its stoop to earth,
was seen to rise hurriedly into the air and to drop down
lifeless.   Immediately a weasel ran off apparently uninjured, and on being examined the Kestrel was found
to have been bitten in the neck to the death by the four-
footed marauder. . . . A Kestrel is rarely seen on the
ground, and still more rarely is seen walking, for it is
extremely necessary to it that its claws should be sharp
in order to grip and hold its prey.

At times the Windhover pursues large game, and a stalker of my acquaintance told me that he once noted it eating a well-grown young Partridge. It has also been known to devour a Grey Crow, though it would seem hardly likely that it had captured it. A Kestrel has been known, too, to hawk cockchafers in the dusk of an evening.

After the young Kestrels have left the nest, they are led by the parent birds across the moors, and should the family be disturbed, the parents show great anxiety for the welfare of their young, though these may be strong on the wing and able to take care of themselves. Indeed it is often necessary that the young should be well matured at the time they leave the nest, for the nesting rock not unfrequently overlooks a deep pool of some hill burn. Considering that it is a member of the dreaded and hated hawk family, the Kestrel seems to excite curiously little hostility from other birds, certainly not as much, I should say, as the Grey Crow ; but I once saw a Windhover have an extremely bad time of it from a colony of Sea Swallows.

To a certain extent only is the Kestrel a resident in Scotland, and in the north of that country it is merely a summer visitor. On the approach of winter, many of those birds which have nested with us cross the Mediterranean, on the farther side of which their food is said to consist mainly of locusts.

The Kestrel cannot be said to be a bird with an extensive northern distribution. It is absent from the Faroes, and from Iceland, but is found in Norway, though it is doubtful whether it reaches the North Cape.

It is met with in Siberia, but not in the most northerly districts of that country. Farther afield it is found in China, Persia, India. In the mountains of the Caucasus it is common and nests in Palestine. Great numbers pass the winter months in Africa.

Description.—The male Kestrel has the head, rump, and tail slate grey, the tail being tipped with white and having a black bar ; mantle and wing coverts red, spotted with black ; throat white, the rest of the under parts light brown, lined with black on the chest and spotted with black on the flanks ; lower abdomen and under tail coverts white ; cere, space round eye, and legs, yellow. The female has the crown and neck red. Tail red, closely barred with black. The under parts resemble those of the male, but are paler.

The young resemble the female. Very old hen Kestrels tend to resemble the males.

THE RAVEN OR CORBY CROW

CORVUS CORAX

FITHEACH, BIADHTACH (*Gaelic*).
" Tha fios fithich aige " = " He has raven's knowledge."
" Thug na fithich aran ann " = " The ravens brought food."
CORBEAU (*French*) ; RABE, KOHLRABE (*German*).

OF all the birds of the mountain lands, the Raven is the very first to commence her nesting operations. The New Year has not long arrived when she sets about repairing her nest, and before February is over she is covering her eggs on some wild crag, seemingly indifferent to the storms of rain and snow which sweep the hills from time to time. Indeed it may be said that the Raven not infrequently chooses the coldest period of the year for her nesting, a fact, I think, quite remarkable, since there is no apparent reason why the young Ravens should be strong on the wing at a time when the majority of other moorland nesting birds are only commencing to lay. With the Eagle it is different—her young must remain a full nine weeks in the eyrie before they are able to fly, and after that time must be initiated into the secrets of capturing their own prey before the shortening days herald the approach of another winter ; but surely there is no need that the Ravens should set out on their first flight before the closing days of April ? For even admitting the fact that they are not above making a meal off any young bird they should happen to come across, young birds of any description are the exception rather than the rule till the closing days of May.

The Raven has decreased almost everywhere in these islands during the last fifty years. To take an instance,

77

in the county of Aberdeen the species is quite extinct as
a nesting bird at the present day, although towards the
western boundary of the county there is an extensive
area of some of the wildest country in Scotland. The
cause for the disappearance of the Raven from this area
is not easy to account for, but to the removal of the sheep
from the two largest deer forests may, I think, be largely
attributed the fact. But many records are to hand which
show that the Raven has been ruthlessly destroyed almost
everywhere. For instance, in 1780, at Arran, 10s. 6d.
was given for the destruction of each Raven's nest, while
in the case of the Kite only 2s. 6d. was offered. In three
years, from 1837 to 1840, 475 Ravens were killed in Glen
Garry. Previous to 1867 the Raven was very numerous
in Caithness and in Sutherland, and the Hoodie rare. Now
the reverse is the case. From 1870 to 1880, 662 Ravens
were killed in Sutherland alone, and for these birds a
premium of 2s. 6d. per head was allowed, a total of
£82, 16s. in all.

It is only on the west and north-west coasts of Scotland
that the Raven is holding its own, and it is even said that
in some districts of Skye it has driven out the Golden
Eagle from its strongholds. In England the Raven is
nowhere numerous. A few pairs nest annually in Devon
and Cornwall, and in the Border district, but in most
places it is decreasing gradually year by year. In former
times the Raven nested on Arthur's Seat, Edinburgh, but
has long since been banished from the Scottish capital.
For many years, too, a pair bred in the Mausoleum at
Castle Howard, Yorkshire. It is curious that a certain
rocky gorge, well known to the writer, should have been
the unfortunately-chosen nesting site of a pair of Ravens
and Golden Eagles in succession. The Corbies were
banished from the district, and now for years on end the
Eagles have attempted, bravely though misguidedly,

to rear their young in spite of great persecution from the keepers of the district.

During the spring of 1914 I had the opportunity of studying more than one pair of Ravens in a certain hill district, during which time I succeeded in obtaining the photographs which illustrate this chapter. Altogether three eyries were visited. In each case the nest was placed on a rock in a most exposed position, at altitudes of between one and two thousand feet above sea-level, and was inaccessible except by the aid of a rope, although it was possible to look into it from above. In each case, too, the nesting site had been used every year by the same pair of Ravens or their descendants, and it was interesting to see that, like the Golden Eagle, the owners of the rock had two nests which, presumably, they used during alternate seasons. In the nesting site first visited by the writer and a companion the Ravens showed signs of great uneasiness while we were yet some distance from the rock, so it was with surprise that we found the nest empty, though freshly lined with wool and grass. Quite a month previously the nest had been in the same condition, so the inference drawn was that the eggs had been removed by some collector. From the interest shown by the Ravens in their nesting site, it seemed possible that the hen bird contemplated a second clutch of eggs, although the season, for the Raven, was already far advanced.

The Corbies were not the only occupants of the rock : Ring Ouzels winged their way past in the bright sunlight, Wheatears flitted uneasily from boulder to boulder, and a Stock Dove moved backwards and forwards across the face of the rock, anxious to return to her eggs concealed in a fissure near the summit of the cliff.

Some fifteen miles to the westward of the nesting site which I have described above is a rocky glen where a second pair of Ravens have their home. On April 18th I visited the nest, and found it contained four fully-fledged young birds. The nest was placed on a ledge of rock half-way down a cliff perhaps thirty feet in height and faced almost south-west, but, owing to a projecting ledge, the sun did not shine full into the eyrie till comparatively late in the afternoon. As I hoped to secure some photographs under as favourable conditions as possible I waited, hidden among some rocks, in the vicinity of the nest in the hopes that the parent birds would return to their family ; but although they circled overhead uttering short, barking cries, they did not once venture near their young. About four in the afternoon the nest and its occupants were in full sunlight, and the young birds were commencing to feel the heat, opening their bills wide and exposing very red throats as they panted and gasped for breath. A week later— April 25th—accompanied by a kindred ornithologist, I again visited the nest. The day was one of the finest of a memorable month of warmth and sunshine, and the hills were looking at their best as we made our way to the home of the Raven-people.

The parent birds circled out to meet us while we were still some way off, and after a careful stalk through the heather we looked across to the nest without the Raven family being aware of our presence. Some of the brood were standing, others were almost invisible at the bottom of the nest, but when we showed ourselves the more venturesome spirits hurriedly crouched once more. This time it was obvious that the young were in a condition to leave the nest if only a means could be found to persuade them to do so. A succession of stones and lumps of peat thrown in the direction of the eyrie caused the family a good deal of uneasiness, but no more, and so, as a last resource, a shepherd's plaid, tied to a rope, was thrown over the rock and moved up and down in front of the nest. This was more than the youngsters could stand,

A Raven's nest.

and one of the brood flew strongly out across the gorge, settling on the grass on the farther side of the little glen. He was almost immediately followed by a second Raven whose powers of flight were not so fully developed, and who came to ground in some rocks near, while a third member of the family, after holding on grimly by one claw to the nesting ledge for a while, was obliged to let go his hold, and fell to the ground beneath. But the fourth youngster showed no inclination to fly—he had never been much in evidence, and, indeed, during the first visit had been quite overlooked for a while—and pressed himself back against the rock as far out of sight as possible. The parent Ravens, on seeing the departure of their family in so unceremonious a fashion, circled nearer, barking repeatedly, and this barking was increased when I descended and attempted to photograph the representative who had fallen from the nest. This young Raven was, I think, the largest and most vigorous of the brood, and as I approached set up the most discordant and terrified croaking cries imaginable, cries which reminded me forcibly of the callings of the Solan Geese on that well-known nesting site of theirs, the Bass Rock. My companion, in the meantime, had secured a second Raven, and after extreme patience and much difficulty we succeeded in obtaining a series of photographs of them standing together on a rock.

During this time what I imagine must have been the mother Raven had alighted on the farther side of the glen beside the young bird who had flown first and most successfully, and seemed to be attempting to persuade the small person to fly. It was then we noticed that the adult birds were accompanied by a third Raven, which I believe had only recently escaped from captivity —having been taken from the same nest some seasons before—and had attached itself to the family, probably

F

for the sake of companionship. This bird took only a mild interest in the fate of the nestlings, contenting itself with perching on the top of a rock or flying about quietly at a considerable distance from the nest.

The sun was now shining with great heat on the slopes of the glen, drawing out the scent of the heather and other hill plants, so that the air was filled with that aroma so pleasing to every lover of the moorlands. The young Ravens were considerably distressed by the heat, gasping and panting for breath, so in order not to cause more anxiety than necessary to the parent birds, we crossed the glen and lay down to watch the course of events. The afternoon was drawing on. Scarce a breath of wind stirred, though light breezes at times crossed from the north, relieving for a moment the sun's heat. On the far hills a heather fire was burning. Flying swiftly up the glen came a pair of Curlews, looking, beside the Ravens, strangely diminutive birds, and a little later came a third Curlew. He was evidently a male bird, for, as he flew, he rose and dipped with that characteristic flight of the nesting season, uttering that singularly charming call note of his which adds so great a fascination to the moorlands in spring.

The Ravens were now circling closer to their crag. Time after time one of the birds lighted on a particular ledge of rock, but seemed unwilling to settle on the ground near its young—possibly previous unpleasant experiences of traps made it disinclined to alight at the foot of the rock. Meantime I could see through the glass that one of the young Ravens was dozing comfortably on a stone, having evidently quite forgotten its trying experiences at the hands of the photographer a short while before. The behaviour of the solitary occupant of the nest was interesting. Before, when his three brothers and sisters shared his home with him, I have shrewd suspicions that he had a comparatively poor time of it—he was scarcely visible in the nest, being sent to the wall by his more vigorous companions, and from his small size I suspect that his share of the food provided was small. Thus, when he discovered himself in complete and undisputed possession of the home, his satisfaction was evident. Through the glass I could see him walking about the nest with a confident air which I am sure he had assumed only during the last few hours. Then, whether the pangs of hunger had commenced to assert themselves, or merely to pass the time, the youngster began to pick up various heather stalks lining the nest, moving about restlessly the while.

After a time he became wearied and settled down at the bottom of the nest, where he was almost invisible from my point of view. A shepherd and his dog crossing the hill scared the parent Ravens away once more and so we left our position and moved down to the lower grounds.

A word as to the notes of the Raven. Compared to his smaller relative, the Grey Crow, his alarm note is quiet and dignified ; he never shrieks harshly like the Hoodie. The usual note of the Raven when his nesting site is approached is a short gruff note uttered in a very low key and reminding one forcibly of the barking of a dog. As well as this cry the Raven makes use, though less frequently, of a liquid call which resembles the drawing of a cork from a bottle.

A third eyrie which I visited about the time of which I write was situated close on 1800 feet above sea-level in a north-facing rock. Two nests were near each other, one evidently the spare nest and in disuse, the other newly lined with wool. Of the birds there was no sign, and I think there can be little doubt but that the eggs had been stolen. It was wild weather when I visited the eyrie ; a strong wind from the west was lashing into foam the waters of the loch in the valley below, but at the Corbie's crag the air was quiet, though the rush of wind at the top of the gorge and the skurrying clouds showed the strength of the air current. Soon a heavy squall of rain and sleet swept across, and immediately afterwards I saw two Ravens come over flying at great speed down wind. They showed a complete lack of interest in the nesting site, however, and crossing to the far side of the glen, turned and flew slowly up against the gale, moving just above the surface of the hill in order to shelter themselves as far as possible from the storm. From their behaviour I had little doubt that their eggs had been stolen, for the nesting site is known to many and the difficulties in affording adequate protection to the birds during the nesting season are great. The nest of the Raven seems to be always built of heather sticks as a foundation; sticks usually taken from a piece of moor which has been burnt only superficially, perhaps, owing to the strength of the wind or some other cause. The eggs repose on a lining of dried grass and wool, and the latter must be of considerable value in retaining the heat during the absence of the mother bird on the wild days of early spring. The eggs, resembling those of the Grey Crow, but larger in size, are from four to six in number, but as many as eight have been found. They vary a good deal in colour; some are pale blue with a greenish tinge and faint blackish underlying shell markings and dark surface spots scattered over the shell; others are olive green, closely marked with blackish brown blotches. It is said that the eggs of the Raven taken in Spain are rather more brightly coloured than those from Northern Europe. In size they vary from $1\frac{29}{40}$ by $1\frac{12}{40}$ to $1\frac{39}{40}$ by $1\frac{13}{40}$ inches.

The Raven frequently nests in trees on the Continent, though on the British Isles it is—nowadays, at all events—

rare to find one in such a position. In Palestine the nest is found on mosques and ruined towers. The young Ravens are hatched out sometimes as early as the middle of March, and must be extremely hardy, since no instance of their deaths from exposure has been recorded so far as I am aware. The chicks are at first of a blackish colour, scantily covered with soft loose greyish black down. As they approach maturity, however, there is little difference, except in size, between young and old, but the young are perhaps less glossed. In the more southern of its nesting haunts the Raven takes her young out into the world before the close of April ; farther north—in the Hebrides, for example—it is the middle of May before they are fully fledged. But though the young leave the nest so early the family, old and young, keep together throughout the summer, the mother bird showing a great amount of affection for her brood. The male bird, too, when his mate is sitting, dashes indiscriminately, after the approved manner of the Green Plover, at any bird which approaches the nesting site, and when the intruder has been put to precipitate flight, shoots back to the nest, croaking with pleasure. It is said also that, like the Lapwing, the male Raven turns completely on his back as he utters his cries.

Toward the end of July I once had an excellent sight of a brood of seven Ravens near the summit of Ben Nevis, and at a height of well above 4000 feet. The day was a cloudless one, and only the faintest of airs played about those great precipices of Scotland's highest hill. The Ravens when disturbed gave me an exhibition of soaring powers which I have rarely seen, equalled except by the Golden Eagle, sailing and dipping in the sunlight with scarcely a motion of their wings before coming to rest, one by one, on a spur about half a mile from me, where they commenced to move actively

about on the stony ground, evidently discovering a food
store even on this barren ridge.

The Raven, like the Grey Crow, has a hatred of the
Golden Eagle which is quite noteworthy, since the King
of the Hills rarely, if ever, attacks a member of the Crow
family. To the attentions of a single Raven the Eagle
takes but little heed, but the attacks of a number of these
birds are a serious menace, and, as I mentioned earlier in
this chapter, the Golden Eagles in a certain district in
Skye have, it is said, been quite driven away by the
Corbies. In the forest of Gaick no fewer than twenty-
three Ravens were on one occasion seen mobbing an
Eagle.

The Raven, though now extremely rare on the eastern
and central districts of Scotland, is not uncommon to the
west, in the land of the great sheep farms. This may, I
think, be partly attributed to its fondness for sheep.
A strong or healthy member of the flock a Raven will
never venture to attack, but should an unfortunate sheep
fall sickly, the bird of ill-omen will watch for days till the
animal dies, dragging out the eyes and tongue of the
victim even before the last breath has left its body. The
bird has been given the name of Tempest-loving Raven,
and rightly so, for no gale is too fierce, no storm too wild
to restrain it from flying over the moors on the look-out
for carrion. At such times it wings its way only a few
feet above the ground, its powerful wings propelling it
forward against the heaviest wind.

It is not known whether in its hunt for food the Raven
is guided by scent or by its keen vision. Although its
favourite food is carrion, it is omnivorous. Young or
sickly birds are not infrequently carried off, and hares
and rabbits are attacked during severe snowstorms,
when they are in an enfeebled condition. Shepherds
state that the Raven will at times murder young lambs,

and it is not above killing poultry and sucking eggs ; but except along the western coast it is now so scarce that the damage done by it can be merely infinitesimal. A dead whale thrown upon the shore becomes the point of attraction to all the Ravens for many miles round, and they feed greedily on the carcase. Sometimes, when its more tasty food fails it, the Raven is reduced to feeding on grubs, insects, and worms, but considering that the young are fed largely on carrion, those I have examined have been in a singularly clean condition.

When eating a dead sheep, perhaps with various species of Sea Gulls sharing in the feast, the Raven retires for a short distance on the arrival of an Eagle, waiting till the King of Birds has eaten his fill before venturing back. When the carcase is that of a larger animal, the Corbies do not fly off although an Eagle, or even a dog, should appear on the scene. A large herd of grampuses having been driven ashore by the inhabitants of Pabbay, in the Sound of Harris, an amazing number of Ravens assembled from all quarters and continued for several weeks to subsist upon the carcases. When this food supply was exhausted, the inhabitants of the district became alarmed lest the birds should commence to feed on their barley. Efforts to drive them away were ineffectual, and matters had begun to look serious when a villager thought of what was really a very ingenious scheme for the removal of the unwelcome visitors. He succeeded in catching some of the Ravens alive, plucked out all their feathers with the exception of those of the wings and tail, and liberated these fearsome-looking scarecrows among their companions. The Ravens, terrified by their mutilated brothers, took their departure in a body, nor did they return again to the district.

A Highlander once remarked to MacGillivray, that famous naturalist of the early nineteenth century, " What

a brave soldier the Raven is! He fights the Eagle, who
is four times his size." In fact, in some districts of the
west coast of Scotland shepherds and farmers used to
welcome the Corbie, enemy to their flocks as he was,
for it was he who drove off the hated Sea Eagle, which
worked so much damage among their lambs.

The Raven has from olden times been looked upon
askance, as a bird of ill-omen. In the Hebrides, however,
it is not viewed as boding death to the household which it
may chance to visit. Still, it is, or was, considered unfortunate for a marriage party to sight a Corbie unless
it should be killed, when the ill-luck is removed and the
omen is even a good one.

The propensity of the Corbie for carrying off the most
curious odds and ends is well known. The late Duke of
Argyll was watching a Raven circling overhead when he
saw it drop something from its bill. The object discarded proved to be a cone from the silver fir—*Abies
pectinata*—on which was growing a parasitic plant known
as *Phelonites strobilina*. This plant has been rarely
found; as a matter of fact, the British Museum was without a specimen, so to it the cone with its parasite was
presented.

What, I think, is an intensely interesting fact in the
history of the Raven is the use to which it was put by
the ancient Scandinavian mariners. When pursuing a
voyage of discovery, and uncertain as to their course and
out of sight of land, though imagining it to be near, a
Raven was let loose from the ship. If he left the vessel,
his line of flight was followed by the boat, and it was rare
indeed for the "dark bird" to play the mariners false,
for by following the direction of the pilot they were en-
abled to reach land and find a harbour. Sometimes,
however, the Raven, after a preliminary flight, returned
to the ship, and when this was the case, it was judged

that land was far off. Legend, indeed, has it that Iceland owes its discovery to the Raven.

The Raven was the sacred standard of the great Odin, and was the inseparable companion of the devastating progress of the Sea Kings. In the Sagas it is stated that Odin possessed two Ravens which traversed great distances and, returning to their master, whispered in his ear the information they had gained during their travels. In this country the Raven was formerly put to a less picturesque use, for in the old coaching days it was customary to keep a tame Raven at the posting houses, and when any traveller drove up, the Corbie would generally call for the hostler.

The age to which the Raven lives is a matter of doubt, but still he has the reputation of being a long-lived bird. A Raven shot near Stockholm in 1839 had a plate on its beak with the date 1770 engraved on it, so presumably the bird had lived for 60 years after it had been branded. Though in earlier days it was generally understood that the term Corbie was applied to Ravens, and to Ravens alone, this cannot always have been the case. An old rhyme has it :

> " D'ye ken the hoose o' Sir William Forbes,
> Surrounded by trees a' black wi' Corbies,
> Frae whence the Pentland Hills are seen,
> Covered wi' sheep, for ever green."

" Corbies " evidently here refers to the common Rook, but still I think this must be rather an exceptional instance of the use of the word.

The Raven is one of the most widely distributed of birds, being found throughout Europe, Asia, and North America, but more numerously in the northern than in the southern parts of these continents. It is found nesting in Greenland, Iceland, and in the Faroes, while in Scandinavia it is common. In the High North it is comof the night in the hope that she will return to the nest and offer a chance of a shot.

On a certain occasion a Hoodie had her young on a grouse moor. The keeper on whose beat the outcasts had made their appearance constructed a "hide" in the vicinity of the nest and waited for many hours in the hopes that the parent birds would return with food for their family and would offer the chance of a shot. But they never put in an appearance, and so the keeper cut off the top of the tree with the nest on it, placed it on the ground, and set traps round it. The strategy was successful, and before long both parent birds were accounted for.

But fortunately for the Hoodie, there are two sanctuaries still open for it in Scotland—one on the coasts, the other amongst some of the wilder deer forests where the Grouse are discouraged, and where for this reason the Grey Crow may even be looked upon with favour. Here the birds remain throughout the year in comparative safety, but immediately they extend their ranges to the neighbouring grouse moors a most hostile reception awaits them.

The reputation of the Grey Crow is certainly not a savoury one. He is an inveterate thief, and during the nesting season he is ever on the alert to pick up and carry away the eggs of any Grouse who has left her nest unguarded while she is away feeding. These ill-gotten trophies the Hoodie bears off—carrying them in his bill —to some moss or burnside, where he helps down his repast with draughts of water. He does not confine his unwelcome attentions only to birds—a newly-dropped lamb or a sickly ewe may be set upon by a number of Grey Crows, and the unlucky victim's eyes pulled out while the breath is still in its body. To the shepherds of the western coasts the bird is the embodiment of evil. To them he is *An t-eun Acarachd*—" the bird without compassion "—and they name him truly indeed.

Disputes have for long been chronicled as to whether the Grey Crow and the Carrion Crow are distinct species. They interbreed it is true, but their range is not the same, and there is, I think, no doubt that they are quite separate species. Vast hordes of Scandinavian Hoodies cross the North Sea on the easterly winds which presage the coming of winter, and spread over the eastern coasts of England, but they are merely winter visitors, and depart again with the spring. The Carrion Crow, on the other hand, is found nesting throughout England where suitable localities occur; even on the outskirts of London it may be seen nesting in isolated trees. It is not many years ago since a Hoodie mated with a Carrion Crow and the pair constructed their nest on the summit of a fir—*Abies nobilis*—on our ground. The hen was of the Grey species; she had seemingly come from a part of the world where little consideration had been shown her, for she was extremely wary, and left the nest every time the front door was opened. It was probably the result of this nervousness, and of the consequent prolonged absences from her nest, that none of the eggs hatched out, though when two species intermate the eggs are not always fertile.

The nest of the Grey Crow is usually—at all events in the eastern and central districts of Scotland—placed in a tree, a birch or Scots pine being the site generally chosen. It is thus curious that the famous Scottish ornithologist MacGillivray, writing early in the nineteenth century, should never have heard of them nesting in such a position. Either the Hoodie must have changed his habits greatly during the last hundred years, or MacGillivray can scarcely have been acquainted with the extensive forests of Ballochbuie and Mar. At times the nesting spot is a ledge of rock, and on the west coast of Scotland this is indeed the usual situation. It is a point of interest that I have never seen the nest in such a position inland,

Hoodie never sights him without giving immediate chase. The young Hoodies grow rapidly, and it is during their youth that their parents make such inroads into the eggs of the Grouse nesting near. These stolen eggs are never taken to the nest itself; they are swallowed by the adult Crow and are regurgitated for the young. It is after the storms of snow that frequently sweep over the higher hills during the month of May that the Hoodies have their greatest feast. Such a storm causes many of the higher-nesting Grouse, Ptarmigan, and Golden Plover to leave their nests, and after the storm has passed and the snow has melted the Hoodies patrol the moors, reaping a rich and incidentally harmless harvest. Truly it is an ill wind that blows good to none.

In a deer forest the Grey Crow has his uses. Many an old or sickly deer falls a victim to the rigours of winter, and were it not for the Hoodies, its body would long encumber the ground. Then again, in autumn when a stag is shot and " gralloched," the entrails are left on the hillside, and so sure are the Crows of the impending feast, that shortly after the report of the rifle they may be seen winging their way from various parts of the hill towards the spot whence the report came. To quite a number of stalkers the Hoodie is known as " the Raven." A friend of mine, on making his first visit to Scotland's largest deer forest, inquired of a stalker whom he met whether the Raven was common in the district. Now, as a matter of fact, it is almost unknown hereabouts, so that when my friend was informed that the " ground was black wi' Ravens," he was in considerable perplexity, till he realised that the " Ravens " were Grey Crows. In this forest the Hoodies are exceptionally numerous during the nesting season, but during the winter some of them at least must migrate to the coast, where food is much more plentiful than at an elevation of from

1000 to 2000 feet above sea-level. By March they have returned to their nesting sites among the hills.

The call of the Hoodie is a sound which, in the stillness of the forest, is heard at a great distance, especially during the quiet of the evening, when there is a great silence over the woods and glens of the hills. An hour or so after the sunset of an autumn night I was making my way down a mountain glen. The frost was already holding the ground, and was hardening the newly-fallen snow, which lay where the sun had failed to reach it during the short hours of his appearance. The afterglow in the west was throwing out in bold relief the bleak plateau of Monadh Mor, and the rocks of Carn a'Mhaim seemed blacker by reason of the snow which covered the heather-clad slopes. It was from these rocks there now were thrown out curious deep barking cries, cries which one might imagine might proceed from a restless spirit roving the hills. Or could it be that a stag had fallen from the rocks, and had injured himself to the death? The call notes were quite unlike anything I had ever before heard, and it was with a feeling almost of incredulity that I discovered from a nearer approach that they came from an old Hoodie who had taken up his station for the night on those dark rocks. In the great deer forest where this incident occurred the Hoodie is permitted to live out his life in quietness : here the fox, the magpie, even the sanguinary stoat and weasel are spared, and the balance of nature is left undisturbed. But from this forest the Grey Crows spread out into the land north, south, east, and west. Here they are at first unsuspecting, not knowing that every man's hand must be against them, but even the most constantly-practised wariness does not save them from an untimely end.

When a Grey Crow's nest has been robbed, and yet the owners have escaped, they wander far and wide over the moors, searching for the eggs or the young chicks

G

THE PTARMIGAN

LAGOPUS MUTUS

GEALAG BHEIRNE, IAN BAN AN-T SNEAC, TARMACHAN, TARMACHAN
SNEACAG, GEALAG BHEINNE, TARMACHAN CREAGACH (*Gaelic*); LAGO-
PÈDE MUET (*French*); ALPEN SCHNEEHUHN (*German*); FJAL RIPE
(*Norwegian*); KURŪNA (*Finnish*).

ASSOCIATED as it must always be with Nature in her most
grand and noble forms, the Ptarmigan appeals to the
ornithologist with a force equalled by few indeed of our
British birds. Instilled into the Tarmachan of the Gaels
is the very essence of the hill country—it would seem
to be inseparable from the steep hill faces and gloomy
corries where Nature is yet in her most primitive state.

Ptarmigan live out their quiet unobtrusive lives removed far apart from the world. As was truly written
by a recent writer—an authority on the Gaels and their
traditions—fires might ravage the country far and wide,
cities might fall before the sword, yet the Ptarmigan would
not know, would not care. It is rare that they even see
the figure of a man except, maybe, a wandering shepherd
or a stalker out after a stag on the highest grounds. It
may be that this want of knowledge of the human character has not a little to do with the extreme tameness
which they often show. There are times, notably in dull,
quiet weather and during the calm of an early summer
morning, when it is almost impossible to induce the Tarmachan to take wing. One such occasion I recall on a
morning of July. Crossing a stony hill-face about 5 A.M.,
we disturbed a covey of Ptarmigan. Instead of rising
from the ground, the birds walked reluctantly forward

only a few yards in front of us, and directly we diverged from their line of retreat squatted quietly among the rocks. Another experience I had of the White Grouse occurred on August 14th, 1913, on Ben Mac Dhui. The birds—a cock and a hen—were on the summit plateau at a height of quite 4200 feet above sea-level, and showed such extreme tameness, refusing to take wing as I approached, that I was able to observe their state of plumage and to notice that in both cases the legs had already assumed the winter covering of white feathers.

During windy weather Ptarmigan are sometimes difficult to approach, but this is by no means always the case, as I have been able to walk to within a few yards of a pack on an open hillside with a strong wind sweeping across from the west.

In the Ptarmigan country it is late before spring arrives to thaw the frozen wastes and to liberate the hill burns from the grip of the ice. In fact, it may be said that there is no real spring on the high hills, only winter and summer. For days, maybe, during the month of April the mountain-tops are shrouded in driving storm clouds and the plateaux are swept with blinding blizzards of snow. Even in May these blizzards often continue, and at the beginning of this month the high hills of the Ben Nevis and Cairngorm range not infrequently carry a greater covering of snow than during any other time of the year. Then, in mid-May, perhaps with little or no warning, weeks of northerly winds and arctic conditions give place to cloudless days, when the sun shines forth from a sky of azure blue and when, under the influence of the strong rays of sunlight and of soft currents of wind from the south, the snow disappears rapidly from even the highest grounds. All life is quick to respond to the change. The Dotterel and the Wheatear arrive to mark out their nesting sites for his flight. As she rose she was almost at once joined by the cock, and the birds took up their station about 200 yards from me. The nest contained eight eggs, laid in a hollow of exceptional depth, and during the time I was photographing my find, both the owners kept up a succession of soft croaking cries of anxiety. The eggs of this nest disappeared mysteriously a short time after my visit, but for a number of years the nesting hollow was clearly visible, and could, I believe, even now be identified.

The nest of the White Grouse is merely a hollow, usually shallow, but sometimes of considerable depth, as in the case just mentioned, scraped on the hillside amongst plants of the crowberry—*Empetrum nigrum*—or the short Alpine grasses which flourish on the high hills. It is never, so far as my experience goes, placed at a lower level than 2500 feet above the sea, and as a result is comparatively seldom found in heather. I have only on one occasion found a Ptarmigan brooding in long heather, and, strangely enough, she was more wild than any of her neighbours who were covering their eggs quite unprotected on the bare hillside. It may be worth while recording here that I have endeavoured as far as possible to fix the upward limit of growth of the common heather—*Calluna vulgaris*—in this country, and from these observations place its greatest elevation on the western slopes of Ben Mac Dhui, where it is met with up to a height of 3300 feet above sea-level, though rarely flowering near the limits of its range. Though the Ptarmigan never nest on the lower hills, they are rarely found at the 4000 foot level— in fact, I do not remember having discovered a nest at a greater altitude than 3600 feet, though the parent birds move up with their broods even to the highest tops (4300 feet) when the weather is fine. The nest is sometimes scraped out between two stones, which afford the brooding bird a certain amount of shelter, but is often extremely exposed, and in such a position that the mother Ptarmigan must sit out quite unprotected from the strong gales and heavy rainstorms which so often sweep the high hills. I have found it to be the case, however, that north-facing hill slopes are avoided during the nesting season. The nest is often lined with a few pieces of lichen—the " reindeer moss " being often chosen—or stems of dead grass, and may contain a number of snow-white feathers from the parent bird ; for the latter at the time of incubation is in the midst of her first moult. I do not, however, think that she deliberately uses her feathers for this purpose.

The eggs, as a rule, number from six to nine, though as many as seventeen have been found. I imagine, however, that this exceptional clutch was the product of two hens. The eggs are laid daily, and incubation is usually commenced before the number is complete. Until the mother bird has actually commenced to brood she covers her eggs, on leaving the nest, with grass and lichen ; but this covering is not done in so thorough a manner as by the members of the Duck family—so imperfectly, in fact, that two or three of the eggs may still remain visible. The eggs so closely resemble those of the Red Grouse that I doubt whether it is possible to distinguish them apart, though they may at times be slightly smaller in size, the measurements being 1·7 inches by 1·1 inches.

As far as I have been able to determine, the period of incubation is three weeks—that is, slightly longer than that of the Red Grouse—owing, perhaps, to the lower temperature which prevails on the high hills. The mother Ptarmigan sits more closely than any British bird. I have erected a cairn at a distance of four feet from a Ptarmigan on her nest, and have secured several photographs of her from this improvised stand, without disturbing her, as far as could be seen. A brooding Ptarmigan has been discovered between the legs of a pony during a halt for lunch, and on another occasion by a dog sitting down on the mother bird. I remember on one occasion discovering a Ptarmigan just as my foot was descending right on the top of the unfortunate bird, who was crouching with eyes half closed beneath me. Even the collapse of a heavy half-plate camera beside her has failed to induce a Ptarmigan to leave her eggs, and I heard an instance of a stalker removing an egg from the nest while the bird was brooding.

The nest is often placed in close proximity to a snow-field, where, on hot sunny days, the hen bird probably cools herself. On two occasions I have found a Ptarmigan's nest beneath the shelter of a stone. The position is unusual, and the birds may have had a definite idea of protection in this sheltered site, for in one instance Common Gulls daily patrolled the hillside, taking heavy toll of unprotected eggs, and in the second case the nest was only a few hundred yards from a Golden Eagle's eyrie. That this precaution was not superfluous may be gathered from the fact that I have more than once seen a Ptarmigan's nest with some of the eggs lying outside. This had, I imagine, been caused by the hurried flight of the birds, and the feather of an eagle lying near explained this quick departure—in one case, at all events. On an average season and at a fair average elevation— 3000 feet—the first eggs are laid about May 20th, and a week later incubation is commenced. During the ensuing period the cock bird mounts guard on some prominent boulder near by, and by repeatedly croaking cries warns his mate of the approach of danger.

When a cock Ptarmigan is flushed under these circumstances, he flies only a short distance—not infrequently in a circle—before alighting on some rock and watching the intruder with considerable anxiety. I remember once

PTARMIGAN BROODING ON HER EGGS.

disturbing a hen Ptarmigan from her nest without the cock having apparently realised the proximity of danger. He immediately flew down from the hillside above and joined his mate, the two birds walking together a short distance before me—the hen, sober and dejected, her husband more erect and soldierly, with head thrown well back, and tail spread fanwise. I have seen, on such occasions, the male bird apparently in conversation with his mate, and evidently remonstrating with her on her lack of courage in leaving her nest.

The young birds are able to move about actively from the first few hours of their existence. They are said to be able to fly at the age of eight days, but I consider this to be an exaggeration, though they are strong on the wing when only slightly larger than Larks. It is written that soon after the young are hatched the cock birds betake themselves to the highest tops, where they join other bachelor friends, returning to the brood when the young can fly strongly, and my own observations especially during 1914 lead me to suppose that this is, sometimes at least, the case.

No bird is so dependent on the weather during the nesting season as the Ptarmigan, and a really satisfactory year for them is an extreme rarity. I do not think I exaggerate when I say that 50 per cent. of the higher-nesting birds lose their eggs or young during an average season, and probably this estimation is considerably short of the mark. During no month in the twelve is the possibility removed of a snowstorm descending without warning on the high hills. Often the last days of June or the first days of July see a north-easterly wind with driving snow squalls blotting out the higher hills, and these storms have a disastrous effect on those younger Ptarmigan which are not of a sufficiently mature age to fly to lower levels.

As I have mentioned, the hen Ptarmigan are in the

habit of taking their broods to the highest plateaux during fine summer days, and on one occasion while walking across the summit of Braeriach (4248 feet above sea-level) I disturbed a hen Ptarmigan with her brood near the edge of a precipice over 1000 feet high. Though the young were incapable of powerful or long-sustained flight, a number of the family made straight for the rocks, disappearing from view in the corrie beneath, while the parent bird betrayed signs of great alarm. I have often wondered what is the procedure on the part of the mother bird on such occasions. It is obvious that those of her family already at the foot of the precipice or clinging to ledges some distance from the top are quite unable to regain the summit, so the mother of the chicks must either induce those of her brood still remaining above to make the exacting flight, or else must leave a number of her progeny for good and all.

It is a matter of interest how rarely one comes across coveys of young Ptarmigan even approaching the number of eggs laid by the birds. At comparatively low elevations—that is, from 2500 to 3000 feet—broods are of good size, consisting perhaps of six or seven birds, but above 3000 feet, I doubt whether the number of young in a family would average four. This is the more worthy of notice since Ptarmigan are excellent mothers, and can invariably be called up, when they have a brood in the vicinity, by the imitation of the alarm note of a chick in distress. On many occasions I have deceived the mother Ptarmigan by this method, and have repeatedly called her to within a few yards of me. Once I remember a Ptarmigan, which I realised from her behaviour must have young, climbing a rocky hillside above me. Here, standing on a narrow ledge of rock, she remained quietly till I used the distress cry of one of her family. The parent in her anxiety over-balanced herself, falling several yards

before she succeeded in flying out over the rock and down
to my feet. On such occasions the birds have run round
me in a circle, trailing their wings and crouching low—
taking advantage during all this time of any shelter they
may happen to pass—and uttering a curious squeaking
cry of distress periodically.

On account of the precarious nature of their nesting,
many young Ptarmigan are found till mid-July in the
downy stage. I have myself seen a young bird with
undeveloped tail towards the end of September; and in
1913, on July 10th, I came across a brood of six Ptarmigan
not more than a couple of days old, while I heard of a
brood being found in a similar state on the 24th of that
month. Young Ptarmigan much resemble Grouse, though
rather smaller and of a more golden tint, but the nature
of the ground on which they are found is usually sufficient
to identify them. Although certain Ptarmigan do lay a
second time, this is by no means always the case when the
first clutch has been destroyed, and many of the White
Grouse in this position form into packs of, maybe, 100
birds as early as the commencement of July.

Besides the damage done to the eggs and young of the
White Grouse by unseasonable falls of snow, a considerable number of eggs are devoured by Grey Crows and
Common Gulls. Both these birds bear off their booty
in their bills to some loch or hill burn where they wash
down their meal with draughts of water. I once visited
a colony of Common Gulls where they nested on a wild
hill loch, and found, in the shallow water, the remains of
eggs of Grouse and Ptarmigan. This might point to the
fact that the young Gulls were sometimes fed on an egg
diet—the suggestion is given for what it is worth.

The Grey Crow is an inveterate egg-stealer, as is also,
in the more western districts, the Raven. The hill fox
not infrequently surprises the Ptarmigan as she broods

spend more time feeding than Grouse, and this may be
due to the fact that the vegetation growing at the high
altitudes frequented has not the same powers of nutri-
ment as that of the lower-lying moors.

There is, I suppose, no bird more fitted to withstand
a mountain snowstorm than the Ptarmigan, and as a
matter of fact an average snowfall leaves them unaffected,
provided there has been sufficient wind to blow some of
the more exposed feeding-grounds free of snow. Thus
an experience I had of the behaviour of the birds during
a blizzard of exceptional severity may be worth setting
down.

I was anxious to study the Ptarmigan in their winter
surroundings, and for this purpose spent a week in a rough
bothy far up an outlying glen in one of the wildest parts
of the Highlands. The morning of the big storm broke
with a southerly wind, bringing with it heavy rain, and
there was nothing to give the least indication of what was
to follow except a very low barometer indeed. During
the morning the glass steadied, the wind shifted right
round to the north, and soft wet snow commenced to fall ;
but notwithstanding this, a mountaineering friend and I
set out for the Ptarmigan ground—a sheltered corrie at
an elevation of some 2500 feet above the sea. As we
reached the corrie the snow thickened and we could see
the drift being blown across the more exposed parts of
the hill in blinding clouds. The frost was now intense,
and our clothes were frozen stiff and so covered with ice
and snow that we must have been in close harmony with
our surroundings, for I was able to stalk a pack of Ptarmigan to within a few feet without the birds being, so
far as could be seen, aware of my presence. As the storm
thickened, we began to realise that quite a migration of
Ptarmigan was taking place into our corrie. The birds
arrived on wing and on foot, those on the wing occasion-

ing a good deal of annoyance to the coveys which chose the slower method of progress. Strong gusts of wind periodically swept the corrie, and the Ptarmigan, as they felt their approach, turned as one bird and, crouching low on the snow, held their ground with great tenacity until a lull allowed them to renew their progress downhill. After a time the birds took wing together, and disappeared from sight towards lower levels ; but here the storm was felt much more severely, and a little later on, when we again disturbed the Ptarmigan, they made for the corrie where we had originally seen them. Out in the open the wind was blowing with gale force, the drift and falling snow rendering progress difficult, and objects only a short way off hard to distinguish.

We reached our shelter before the full force of the storm swept the glen, and it was fortunate that we did so, as the following incident will make clear. Although the darkness had not yet closed in, the drift was so thick that there was a certain element of danger in venturing even a few yards from the door of the bothy ; so a coin was tossed to decide who should make the journey to the well for a fresh supply of water. I succeeded in winning the toss, so my friend set out with a large pail to search for the well. It may be difficult to credit the fact, but so thick was the drift, that in the twenty-five yards which separated well from bothy he several times lost his bearings, and returned five minutes later breathless and exhausted, just as I was debating whether it would be advisable to tune up my bagpipes to guide him back to shelter.

No one who has not actually experienced a hill-storm can form any conception of its severity, and from such an experience one can realise the immense difficulties from this source which beset the Arctic explorers on their marches. I doubt whether, under the conditions which

H

a case is on record—from Skye—of Ptarmigan being met with at less than 100 feet from the sea-level, and as recently as 1913, during a heavy snowfall in Perthshire, they were seen on cultivated land.

In Norway Ptarmigan often follow the reindeer in the winter and dive into the holes made by these animals, thus obtaining a few berries. In winter they roost in the snow, and in my experience even seek out snowfields on which to roost during the summer months, for on such fields in August and September I have frequently found their roosting hollows. Ptarmigan sleep in coveys, but Mr. Millais is of opinion that the birds when roosting together are more scattered than Grouse or Partridges, and I am inclined to agree with him in this.

During the short days of December, when darkness closes in about the hills three hours after noon, the soft calling of the Ptarmigan is singularly in keeping with their surroundings of grandeur. On such a day I have crossed through a wild hill pass, and at the watershed have disturbed a large pack of these White Grouse. The murmur of many snowy wings as the birds wheeled their way above my head from one hill face to another is a sound that will for long be retained as a highly-prized gift of the high hills—given only to those who know and appreciate them in winter gloom as well as under a summer's sun.

When a vegetation composed of blaeberry and crowberry is present, the Tarmachan appear to choose that ground for a home in preference to grass or heather, because, I think, of their preference to the young shoots of the former plants as food.

Ptarmigan in winter are as white as the snowy wastes they inhabit, and I shall always remember the sight I had of a covey of these birds crossing a hill-top in the rays of a setting sun in January. As they emerged from the slopes already in shadow and caught the sun on the plateau, their white plumage was instantly transformed, and the Ptarmigan in their newly-acquired rosy dress, wheeling rapidly past, presented a picture that must ever be retained in the memory. The protective change of plumage on the part of the Tarmachan, while usually of great service to them in avoiding their enemies, has its disadvantages when the winter snowstorms are late in descending on the high hills.

In November, and even in December, snow is sometimes absent from the highest levels, and during times such as these, Ptarmigan offer an easy mark to the Eagle and hill fox, for they stand out against the dark hillsides like miniature snow wreaths, and are visible at a distance of, I should say, a full half-mile. If there should happen to be any fields of snow on the hills, the Ptarmigan frequent these fields throughout the day, venturing off only a short distance to feed. On such a snowdrift every Ptarmigan of that particular hill may resort, knowing that there, and there only, are they protected from the keen sight of the Eagle, for the great bird is constantly sailing on motionless wings across the hill faces during the hours of the short winter day. The presence of a fox does not occasion the same amount of anxiety to these mountain Grouse, but their four-footed enemy accounts for a great number of victims during the course of a winter. On one occasion a fox, chased by a collie dog, appeared to be running with difficulty. Reynard disappeared in some rocky ground, but was routed out and despatched, the body being found to contain no less than three Ptarmigan, including the wings and feathers of the birds.

In Iceland, the Iceland Falcons prey on the Ptarmigan of that island, and there is a fable among the natives that the Falcon screams with agony when, in devouring the Ptarmigan, she finds, on reaching the heart, that she has killed her long-lost sister.

may appear—on the neck; and during March and April
there is a gradual moult of the winter dress, the breast
feathers being the last to appear. I have, however, seen
a specimen still in almost full winter plumage in mid-April.
The winter feathers are gradually lost until, in the last
days of May, the summer dress is almost complete. In
June the males generally show white tips to the feathers
and white feathers still in the tail coverts—where a single
white feather is retained until July. The white tips on the
back and breast of the male have by now worn off, and
the plumage is much darker. In the female the plumage
is more rusty and faded. During the last week of July
the blue grey feathers of autumn make their appearance,
and the feathers fall off the legs. In August both cock
and hen Ptarmigan change to their full autumn plumage,
and at the end of that month the feathers of the feet have
appeared. During September the feathers of both male
and female fade. In October the feathers of the tail and
wings are renewed, and it is stated that at the middle of
this month the first pure white feathers make their appearance, but as far as my personal experience goes, the
commencement of the assumption of winter plumage
takes place a full fortnight before this date; and on the
last day of the month, I on one occasion flushed a cock
Ptarmigan in full winter plumage, so far as could be seen.
In November a few of the old feathers of autumn still
remain on the back and head—by now the feet are fully
covered.

During December, as a rule, the white feathers of the
full winter plumage are assumed. I doubt whether Mr.
Millais is correct in his supposition that the assumption
of winter plumage varies with the mildness of the weather,
though I think that those Ptarmigan living at the highest
levels of their range retain their white dress further into
the spring than those having their homes on hills where

the snow cap breaks up earlier. The cock Ptarmigan of the north of Norway retain much white on their upper parts right through the summer.

Although the Grouse of the high grounds are frequently found nesting in Ptarmigan country, not a single undoubted hybrid has ever been shot in Scotland, though several supposed cases have occurred. A bird which was shot at Kintradwell, Brora, in 1878 presented many hybrid features. The feathers were a perfect blend of the two species, but more than possibly it was merely an uncommonly marked Grouse. It is, indeed, the great range of colour exhibited by this latter bird that makes the identifying of hybrids a matter of great difficulty. Two supposed hybrids were exhibited in 1907 by the British Ornithologists' Union, but their claims are not above suspicion. Still, it is reasonable to suppose that hybrids must occasionally occur.

Several authorities on the Ptarmigan agree that those birds inhabiting the highest plateaux are considerably smaller in size than those nesting at lower levels ; but I must say that my somewhat extended observations have not borne out this theory. This difference in size may be more marked in other countries, for an instance is on record of Ptarmigan being met with at the great elevation of 9700 feet above sea-level.

An interesting method of trapping Ptarmigan in the Highlands is given by Mr. J. G. Millais. I gather, however, that this must now be numbered amongst those old Highland practices which have been lost to us as the result of the more strict game-preserving of recent years. The trapper, armed with a bagful of oats and a beer or—preferably—champagne bottle, makes his way, after heavy snow, to a place on the hill where the Ptarmigan usually congregate. Here he makes a number of indentations in the snow with his bottle, and fills the bottom of

the cavity with grain to just within reach of the birds.
Unless frost comes, the plot must end in failure, but if
the cavity is properly hardened, the birds, after eating the
grain on the surface, attempt to reach that temptingly
displayed in the cavity. In doing so they over-balance
and are held prisoners, for the feathers resist all attempts
at backward progress.

In Lapland Ptarmigan are said to be caught in large
numbers in birch snares. Sometimes the close harmonisation of a hen Ptarmigan with her surroundings may be
against her safety. I have seen on more than one occasion
a herd of deer, moving quickly down a hillside at the
scenting of danger, pass right over the spot where a mother
Ptarmigan was tending her brood. The startled bird ran
forward in front of the stags feigning injury in order to
draw them away from the vicinity—a needless precaution
in the case of excited animals in full flight. The young
Ptarmigan on these occasions run a considerable risk of
untimely death, but they are able to conceal themselves
amongst rocks in a most remarkable manner, and probably
do so on the approach of the herd.

Although, as I have mentioned before, Ptarmigan
are found with their broods even on the very highest tops
during the summer months, they are rarely met with
above the 3000 feet line in winter ; and never, I think,
visit the plateaux about the 4000 feet line at that season
of the year. I am inclined to believe that on the hills
bordering the Atlantic the birds are found regularly at
somewhat lower altitudes than is the case on the Cairngorm range.

There is little doubt, I think, that Ptarmigan make
periodic migrations from one hill to another, and I have
heard that when a certain isolated hill in Aberdeenshire
has been shot over repeatedly, the existing stock of Ptarmigan take wing in a body, making for a hill about a dozen

miles distant and across the Dee Valley. In Labrador great migrations of Ptarmigan have been chronicled, and a specimen has been shot on St. Kilda, an island fifty miles out into the Atlantic off the Hebrides.

The flight power of the Ptarmigan is, I think, superior to that of the Red Grouse ; and the birds can wing their way up a steep hill face at a surprising speed. During recent years Ptarmigan shooting has decreased in popularity, and one rarely hears nowadays of really big bags being obtained. The record shoot took place, I believe, at Achnashellach, where 61 brace were accounted for in a day ; but in 1886 as many as 27 brace were killed on the Forest of Gaick, Inverness-shire, in the course of a single drive. On this forest 60 brace have been shot during a day.

Doubtless the long and strenuous walks up to Ptarmigan ground prevent any but the most enthusiastic sportsmen from decimating the ranks of the White Grouse, and I have never heard a gun fired on the Cairngorm range of hills, which holds, I imagine, the most extensive area of Ptarmigan ground in these Islands. But I do not think that there has been an increase in the number of the birds since I first became familiar with the range, though on the Forest of Gaick, some fifteen miles to the west, their numbers have greatly decreased.

Ptarmigan suffer attacks of the same disease as that which causes such mortality amongst the Red Grouse. In Iceland, according to Henry Slater, the rock Ptarmigan are prone to epidemics similar to grouse disease. There is the same emaciation, featherless legs and toes, and inflammation of the viscera with abundant entozoa. During 1913 grouse disease was more prevalent than for a considerable time, and it is possible that Ptarmigan were also sufferers. At all events, I have rarely seen so few birds as during July of that year, when I was camping out at an elevation of over 3000 feet, right in the heart of the Ptarmigan country. One traversed extensive areas of Ptarmigan ground without coming across a single bird, the cold winds and snowfalls of early June having had a disastrous effect on their numbers. The tendency of the birds to pack early in the summer is, I think, explained by this fact—the unfortunate Ptarmigan which have had their eggs or young destroyed joining up with the barren birds, with the result that extensive packs may be seen shortly after the Longest Day. In mid-July I have seen such a pack, consisting of over a hundred birds, which contained only one young individual.

Although I have frequently called up hen Ptarmigan during the nesting season by imitating the distress cry of their young, I had never succeeded in deceiving the adult birds when free from family cares until quite recently. It was in October on Cairngorm that I first succeeded in effecting this. I flushed a cock which, from his reluctance to move, I surmised must have a mate near, so just to see what would happen, I whistled the high, piercing note which had hitherto deceived the mother birds. Somewhat to my surprise, the Ptarmigan approached, uttering croaking, anxious cries, and remained in the vicinity till I left. I imagine that he thought I had captured his mate, and that the disturbing cries proceeded from her. I mention this partly to show how much more attentive a bird—to its mate as well as to its young—is the Ptarmigan than the Red Grouse; for I am quite certain that the latter bird would not show such devotion in times of danger.

In his *Rough Notes on the Birds observed during Twenty Years' Shooting and Collecting in the British Islands*, Booth gives an interesting account of Ptarmigan-shooting. He found it the safest plan on such occasions to leave the lodge by 3 or 4 A.M., so as to reach the high ground by daylight. An extract from this writer's notes for 1865 is given :

" *December 7th.* —It was well on towards midday before we reached the top of the hill, and on approaching the summit, it was evident that all the surrounding ranges were enveloped in mist which was gradually advancing from the NE. An immediate start in search of birds was consequently made, in hopes of obtaining a brace or two before the mist compelled us to desist. Forming at once into line (two keepers, two gillies, and myself), so as just to keep one another in sight, we made the best of our way round the face of the hill. The surface of the snow being hard and frozen, we were able to advance at some speed, though, of course, walking on the slopes was risky. On reaching a large patch of broken stones on the north side of the hill, perhaps a wee bit over the march (but the mist was so thick it was impossible to tell our whereabouts with any certainty), the croak of a Ptarmigan was heard, and on stopping the line and looking round, I soon made out a white head over some large blocks of stone. Almost immediately it was detected the bird dashed downhill, though just too late to escape, and falling dead rolled to the foot of the rocks. On being recovered it proved to be a young cock, the plumage still exhibiting a large amount of grey among the white feathers. After passing two or three ugly spots where the line was forced to open right and left, we started several birds which were lost sight of in the mist before there was an opportunity of firing a shot. At length during a slight break in the clouds, as the mist was somewhat less dense, a drive was attempted. Taking my station on a ridge on the east side of the hill, the men were despatched right round. One bird only could I discern, though several others passed in the haze. Being uncertain whether the shot had taken effect, we searched the direction which the bird had followed, and found him at once perfectly dead, with the wings spread out, on an open patch of ground from which the snow had drifted. When again going round the hill, some birds were heard croaking a hundred yards or so in front of the line. On making towards the sound, intently examining the outline of the snow to obtain an early view of the pack, a large sheet of ice was overlooked and, my feet slipping, away I went downhill. Luckily there was a drift of newly-fallen snow (soft as a feather bed) about twenty feet below, and into this I pitched quite easily, none the worse, not even a shake. Had it not been for the snow, I must have gone over a hundred feet to the bottom of a steep gully. . . .

" It was now nearly dark, and time to be leaving the hill ; so the keeper called the men together. As two of them were not forthcoming, and had not been seen for over an hour, I fired several shots without, however, the slightest result. . . . As a last resource I fired a few more shots, and we then started downhill, finding no little difficulty in picking our way owing to the uncertain light and extent of the tracts of frozen snow. Luckily our pace was slow, as after proceeding about a couple of hundred yards, a faint cry some distance to the north was audible, during one of our halts. After answering, and waiting a few minutes, the men came up. Both were nearly beat, but a pull at the *Doctor* and a few mouthfuls of food soon revived them. We learned that, while holding the two stations on the line, the poor fellows had been going around the east side of the hill, cutting their way as best they could through a frozen snow-drift, till at last it was discovered impossible to proceed farther, and on turning back they found to their dismay that some fresh snow had fallen over the tracks previously cut ; consequently, owing to the mist and gloom, they were in a decidedly critical position. It was lucky the shouts were heard, as weary and benumbed by cold, they were utterly incapable of reaching shelter even if aware of the line to be followed. A heavy fall of snow commencing as we at last took leave of the mountain-top, it is unlikely that any tidings would have been learned concerning their fate till the snows had melted from the hills in the following summer."

In their colouring Ptarmigan vary considerably, and I am inclined to suspect that the rock Ptarmigan—*Lagopus rupestris*—which is generally held to be a distinct species, and which is reputed to have occurred in Sutherland and Perthshire, is merely a variation of the normal type. *Lagopus rupestris* is more rufous brown in colour than the common Ptarmigan, but in 1912 I found a hen bird sitting exceedingly hard on the lower ground of Braeriach, which in her colouring bore every resemblance to *Lagopus rupestris*, but which was, I have little doubt, merely a variation of *Lagopus mutus*. The total length of *Lagopus mutus* is between 14 and 15 inches, the female being about half an inch shorter than the male, and the birds slightly smaller than the Red Grouse. The length of wing is 7·6 inches, and the weight 20 ounces.

Distribution.—The Ptarmigan is a bird of extremely wide distribution, from the high hills of Scandinavia to the Urals. In North Siberia it is represented by *Lagopus rupestris*, which is found as far north as 71½° N. latitude. In Iceland a sub-species—*Lagopus rupestris islandorum*—is found. The rock Ptarmigan is met with in Greenland, North America, and North, Central, and Eastern Asia ; and similar sub-species exist in Newfoundland, Labrador, Canada, and Alaska. The true Ptarmigan is found in the rhododendron region of the Alps, in the Pyrenees, Tyrol, Styria, and Carinthia, and on the Urals above the limit of the growth of the birch. The eastern range is difficult to determine. It has been obtained from the Chinese Altai range at 6000 feet and round Lake Baikal at 9000

feet.   In Japan it has been reported at the 9250 feet
level.   It occurs in parts of Russia.   It seems to be absent
from the Himalayas and the Andes.   Of the Ptarmigan
found in Europe and North America, the Icelandic form
most closely resembles our own native birds.   In China,
Alaska, and Arctic America numerous forms are found,
while from the mountains of Newfoundland comes a grey
form, resembling our own.   In Spitzbergen a larger form,
Lagopus hypoboreus, occurs, much resembling the Willow
Grouse.

In this country the Ptarmigan is nowadays found no
farther north than Caithness, though it formerly inhabited
the Hoy Hills in Orkney.   Early in the nineteenth century it still bred in the Galloway Hills in the south of
Scotland, and a shepherd told Sir Herbert Maxwell that
in 1826 he saw a Ptarmigan on the Merrick (2700 feet) in
that district.   Recent attempts to reintroduce it there
have been so far unsuccessful.   In the seventeenth century
it was written of the Merrick : " In the remote parts of this
great mountain are very large red deer, and about the top
thereof that fine bird called the Mountain Partridge,
or by the commonalty Tarmachan, about the size of a Red
Cock and the flesh much of the same nature ; feeds as
that bird doth on the seeds of the bullrush, and makes its
protection in the chinks and hollow places of thick stones
from the insults of the eagles which are in plenty, both the
large grey and the black, about that mountain."   Ben
Lomond is now its southernmost limit.   If local rumour
be relied on, a few lived in earlier times in the Lake District, and one, said to have been killed on Skiddaw, was
formerly in a local museum in Keswick.   Doubts have,
however, been cast on these statements on account of the
fact that even nowadays a white mottled variety of the
Red Grouse is to be found in that district so resembling
the true Ptarmigan that it has been taken for this bird

by Scotch keepers. Still I think that, considering that many of the hills in the district are over 2500 feet in height, it is extremely probable that Ptarmigan did actually inhabit them, and that they have shared the fate of the beautiful and confiding Dotterel which has, too, been banished from the district.

THE BLACK GROUSE

LYRURUS TETRIX

Coileach-dubh (Black-cock), Cearc liath (Grey-hen) (*Gaelic*) ; Coq
de Bruyère (*French*) ; Birkhahn (*German*).

THE Black Grouse is more cosmopolitan in its habits than
the Capercaillie. Almost equally at home on the heather-
clad hillside as among the thick forests of pine, it is found
distributed pretty generally through the country of the
hills. Whereas in the Highlands of Scotland the Black
Grouse prefers the forests of pine and the glens wooded
with birches as its country, on the moorlands of Northumberland it frequents the open hillsides, the stone
walls which abound in that district being much sought
after as perching stations, and what woods there are being
apparently avoided.

The most interesting feature in the life of the Black
Grouse is the early morning combats which take place day
after day with great regularity between the cocks of the
species. The same fighting-ground is always frequented,
and the combats are engaged in not only during the mating
season, as might be expected, but during nearly the whole
of the year. In fact, a stalker of my acquaintance who has
had great experience of Black-cock, tells me that they fight
most energetically during cold frosty mornings in early
December.

During the months of July and August there is a lull
in the combats, but with the approach of autumn the
" sparring " is recommenced, though in a milder form
than that witnessed later on in the year. The fighting-

ground of the Black-cock is usually a grass-covered clearance in the forest, but sometimes a young plantation is used, the young trees being beaten to the ground by the constant movements of the birds. In such cases, however, the fighting-ground was probably in existence before the young trees were planted.

To such fighting-grounds the whole of the Black-cock population repair with the first light of the dawn, and immediately commence work. They pace slowly around, crouching low on the ground with their tails spread out to their full stretch, and appear to fight indiscriminately with any member of their species they may happen to approach. An adversary having been obtained, the two cocks face each other with heads bent low and then together fly up perpendicularly into the air, striking at each other with their feet. In moments of excitement, just before springing on each other, I have noticed the Black-cock half open their wings and strike them sharply against their sides. Such a fight as a rule lasts for only a few seconds of time, the birds separating and seeking fresh opponents. Thus fights in deadly earnest are not often seen, but when such fights are engaged in, one of the combatants is sometimes left dead on the field.

There seems to be a very great preponderance of male birds at these fighting grounds, the Grey-hens being outnumbered ten to one. These hens move about the fighting-ground watching the males with quiet interest, their presence causing great efforts to be put forth on their behalf. Sometimes a Grey-hen flies off to the top of a neighbouring pine, and is a spectator of the battle-ground from her elevated perch.

Though the Black-cock are apparently concentrated on their fights, it is no easy matter to approach them, even through the cover of a wood, for they take alarm at the least noise or movement and fly off in a body to the neigh-

bouring forests. Should the cause of their alarm remain
motionless and unseen, they soon return, however, and
immediately they have alighted, fighting is engaged in.
I have noticed that with the rising of the sun the birds
become quieter, and that when the rays fall full on the
fighting-ground, concord is restored between former adversaries. Thus in dark, misty weather sparring is continued later than when the sky is clear, and those gathering-
grounds in the shelter of steep hills, and so cut off from the
sun, retain the birds for a considerable period after sunrise.
For a short time before dispersing the Black-cock feed,
and, should their differences have not been entirely settled,
they retain their tails spread out fanwise even when satisfy-
ing their morning appetites. There is a certain fighting-
ground bordering the river Dee on its upper reaches where
noticeably fewer Black-cock are seen at the present time as
compared with former years. A stalker who spoke to me
on the subject gave it as his opinion that Capercaillie were
responsible for this decrease ; that they had driven out
the black game. While this sounds somewhat improbable,
a colleague of my informant, on a visit to the ground,
found only a few Black-cock present and several cock
Capercaillie on the scene.

When at the fighting-ground—or " lek "—the Black-
cocks utter a soft cooing note which in the stillness of the
early morning carries an extraordinary distance, and is
sometimes extremely difficult to locate and follow up.
When fighting they are said to crow hoarsely from time to
time. One Black-cock mates with a number of Grey-hens,
but takes no part in the duties of rearing the young. In
fact, he leaves his numerous wives before they have deposited their eggs. It is early in May, as a rule, that the
Grey-hen scrapes out a hollow amongst the long heather
carpeting a scattered pine forest, and commences to lay her
handsome eggs. I have remarked that she frequently

chooses the vicinity of a road or stalking path for her nesting site, doubtless with the view to leading her chicks to ground where they can walk without difficulty. Not in-frequently the nest is made under a small pine growing on the outskirts of a wood and surrounded by long heather. It is doubtful whether the depression scraped by the Grey-hen justifies the word " nest " being applied to it. It may, perhaps, be lined with a few blades of grass or pine needles, but when these are present they are, I think, as often as not there by accident.

The eggs number from seven to ten. A description of those of the Capercaillie applies with equal force to them, except that they are smaller in size. Incubation lasts for twenty-four days, and sometimes the mother bird sits very closely. On one occasion I discovered, shortly after a severe May snowstorm, the deserted nest of a Grey-hen containing a solitary egg. I surmised that the second nest must be somewhere near, and shortly after-wards found the Grey-hen sitting on her nest in a thick pine wood. The situation of the nest was an unusual one, and resembled more a Capercaillie's site than a Grey-hen's. The nest was placed beneath a fallen pine branch with no ground vegetation anywhere near, and doubtless the bird had sought the shelter of the wood on account of her first unpleasant experience with the snow.

Although incubation had just been commenced she sat very closely, and I succeeded in approaching her to within a few feet and exposing a number of plates. Nearly three weeks afterwards I again visited her nesting site, expecting that the bird would now sit more closely than on the first occasion, but I found that this was not the case.

Another nest in the neighbourhood from which the young had been hatched contained a couple of eggs which, on being broken, showed well-formed chicks, and had the

Grey-hen brooded a few hours longer she would have hatched off her entire clutch. Like the Capercaillie, however, she seems to be content if she brings off only a portion of her young, leaving the most backward to perish in the shell. That she may, notwithstanding, be a good mother to her young is borne out by an instance which is reported from Ross-shire, where a Grey-hen, rather than leave her brood, perished with her young in a big heather fire. Though the young Black Grouse are able to run actively about a few hours after they are hatched, they do not reach maturity till the latter part of September, so that the opening of black game shooting might be well postponed for a month or even six weeks—from August 20th to September 30th.

The wing power of the Black Grouse is marked. As compared with representatives of the Red Grouse, the birds move their wings more slowly and yet forge ahead more rapidly. Their flight, too, is noticeably even, and there is no rocking and swaying as in the case of the Grouse. Down wind, when once they have got going, they are capable of travelling at a tremendous speed.

The food of the black game is varied. They feed greedily on the young shoots of Scots pine and larch, and are thus serious enemies to afforestation, especially to pioneer afforestation. The land recently acquired by the Government at Inverliever for afforestation purposes is a case in point. Here the black game have caused such injury to young plantations of Scots pine that the planting of these trees has had to be discontinued. The larch plantations have also been greatly damaged, but the larch, having more powers of recovery than the pine, is not destroyed so easily. Black Grouse also feed on the buds of the birch, and are partial to berries of various kinds, notably the blaeberry (*Vaccinium myrtillus*). They eat young heather and blaeberry shoots, also grass seeds, and

GREYHEN ON NEST.

NEST OF THE GREYHEN.

sometimes insects. They are said to be partial to the berries of the rowan (*Sorbus ancuparia*).

When the crofters' oats are left in the stook, owing to unfavourable weather conditions, for a prolonged period, the Black-cocks (not so much the Grey-hens) are frequently to be seen perched on the stooks devouring the grain. They are much more wary than the Grouse which are usually with them, and take flight before the former birds show any signs of suspicion. It is said that sometimes, after partaking of sodden grain, in which fermentation is far advanced, the birds become so intoxicated that they can scarcely rise from the ground, and that their flight on such occasions follows a somewhat erratic and devious course.

The range of the Black Grouse is an extensive one. In Scandinavia, Russia, Germany, and France it is found widely distributed. It occurs in Northern and Central Asia. Unlike the Capercaillie, it has not been reported from the Pyrenees. In the Caucasus an allied species— *Lyrurus mlokosiewiczi*—is found. It is less robust than our representative, and the male's plumage is entirely black. As I mentioned earlier in the chapter, the Black Grouse is met with generally throughout Scotland, but there are one or two districts where it is not known. Though present in the Inner Hebrides, it is non-existent in the Outer Hebridean Islands. Neither is it known in the Orkneys or Shetlands.

Description : Adult male.—General colour black, the feathers of the head, neck, lower back, and rump margined with purplish blue. The outer webs of the outer primary quills pale brown mottled with white, the basal part of the innermost primary and secondary quills pure white, the secondaries being also margined with the same colour. Axillaries under wing coverts and under tail coverts pure white. Thighs showing a good many white feathers.

Wattle scarlet. Bill black. Feet brown. Total length, 23·5 inches ; wing, 10·3 inches ; tail, 8·8 inches ; tarsus, 1·9 inches.

During the summer an " eclipse " plumage is assumed, and the black feathers of the back and sides of the head and nape, and sometimes those of the upper mantle, are replaced by a temporary plumage resembling that of the Grey-hen.

Female.—Top of the head, neck, and back barred with red brown and black, also wing coverts, scapulars, and secondaries. Sides of the head, chin, and throat buff, spotted with black and rufous, and fringed with white. Legs almost white. Under tail coverts white or pale rufous, barred with black and tipped with white. Tail black with markings of red brown and tipped with white. Total length, 17 inches ; wing, 8·9 inches ; tail, 4·5 inches ; tarsus, 1·6 inches. The young when hatched have the crown chestnut bordered with black, forehead and lores buff, with a Λ-shaped patch of black behind the bill. Two wide stripes of light brown surround the crown, and there are also present two dark patches behind the eyes and on the sides of the nape. Wing coverts and rump chestnut. A black band extends down the back of the neck. Cheeks and throat light yellow. Old Grey-hens which have become barren or birds which perhaps were shot in the ovary at times assume a partial male plumage, and there is said to be on record the case of a Black-cock assuming the dress of a Grey-hen.

THE RED GROUSE

LAGOPUS SCOTICUS

CEARC-FHRAOCH, EUN FRAOICH, EUN RUADH (*Gaelic*).

THE one and only bird which Great Britain, and more especially Scotland, can claim for her very own is the Red Grouse, and for that reason alone it occupies an interesting place among our bird population. The ancestry of the Grouse is not known beyond doubt, but it is supposed that the bird has its origin from a species—perhaps the Ptarmigan, more probably the Willow Grouse—which assumed a winter plumage of white, and that this winter dress was gradually discarded owing to an absence of snow during the winter months. If this be indeed the case, the break-away from the Tarmachan must have occurred in earliest times, since nowadays, as I have mentioned, the birds interbreed extremely rarely, if indeed at all.

In the present day, when the tendency amongst ornithologists would appear to be toward breaking up birds into as many sub-species as possible, the Grouse, I venture to suggest, would offer a good field for these scientific researches. In the case of the male bird at least three forms—the red form, the black form, and the white spotted form—are found, while the female, in addition to showing the three above-mentioned types, produces a buff-spotted race and a buff-barred race.

It is not too much to say that the Red Grouse has transformed Scotland during recent times, and I believe that, at the present day, the grouse moors in the country north of the Tweed have a value of not less than £1,000,000.

It cannot be gainsaid that in these big areas under Grouse
socialists bring to bear good material for the advancement
of their claims.	But a fact generally lost sight of—if indeed
it be known to those who decry grouse moors—is that the
very best grouse ground is that which cannot possibly
be put to any other use.	Poor peaty soil in situations
so exposed that it would not support timber, ground
where no sheep could find a living, this is where the
Red Grouse makes a congenial home.	And even on
the lower grounds, wherever one finds moors bearing on
them no grass, it may be taken as an accepted fact
that the ground possesses but little value from the agri-
culturist's point of view.	Though Grouse are numerous
amongst	the	peat	hags	stretching	across	extensive
plateaux 2500 feet above the sea, they are never seen
on the highest hills.	They never indeed exceed, or even
reach, the uppermost limits of the growth of the heather,
and may be said to be entirely absent above the 3000-
foot level.

The birds nesting at or near the 3000-foot line find that
the heather growing at these exposed altitudes affords
but a scant protection to their nests ; they sometimes
brood right out in the open in much the same position
as a hen Ptarmigan chooses for her nest, but notwithstanding that Grouse and Ptarmigan nest sometimes
within a few yards of each other, the two species keep
noticeably distinct.	.	.	.	The Red Grouse is perhaps
the most sedentary of our British birds, and in a sheltered
grouse moor the stock is to be found in more or less the
same situations all the year through.

It is probable, however, that the Grouse nesting towards
the upper limit of their range move down to more sheltered
quarters during severe weather, while a prolonged snowstorm and hard frost at times drive the whole of the birds
from a high-lying moor.	Sometimes, indeed, these birds,

having in their search for food found more congenial haunts, do not return to their former home when the snow disappears, and the moor is greatly depleted of its stock. On only one occasion have I seen a Grouse on migration. This was during a severe storm, which descended with no warning on the high grounds, causing even the hardy Tarmachan no little privations.

Near the top of a pass was some grouse ground at about the 2500-foot level, and from this ground I saw a solitary Grouse winging his way rapidly southward, progressing in a manner which showed that a short flight only was not his aim. It is rare that Grouse frequent the coast-line during migration, but still they have from time to time been recorded at light-stations.

Towards the east coast the country is not, as a rule, favourable to *Lagopus scoticus*, but there is a certain moor with which I am familiar which must, I think, occupy an almost unique position in that it actually touches the North Sea. The moor is a small one, and is surrounded by fertile agricultural land. In summer the situation is favourable enough, but in winter there is an absence of shelter, and wild winds from the sea sweep over the moor, carrying with them driving mist and rain. Here the Grouse have unusual companions to share their nesting-ground. The confiding Eider Duck leads forth her ducklings on the moor, the Stock Dove and the Shell Duck make their nests down the rabbit burrows which everywhere undermine the ground. A colony of Black-headed Gulls, too, nest at the moorside, making periodic egg-plundering excursions, while amongst the sand-dunes thousands of Common Terns and a few of that most swallow-like of the sea-bird tribe, the Lesser Tern, make their homes during the months of summer. The best Grouse country lies undoubtedly towards the centre of Scotland ; as one approaches the Atlantic the proportion of heather on the hills decreases, and its place is taken by various grasses which are not so favourable to the Red Bird.

During fine still days of early January it is interesting to lie concealed on some sunny hill face of a low-lying moor and to watch the mating of the Grouse. One hears on every side the deep guttural calls of the cocks as they " display " before the lady of their choice. Often they rise almost perpendicularly into the air, descending on to some boulder or knoll with loud cries. They are sometimes easy to approach, and even when disturbed are reluctant to take flight. The pairing of the Grouse takes place at such an early date that one or more snowstorms invariably cause the mated birds to reform into packs, but it may possibly be the case that even under such conditions the birds remain paired. The nesting season of the Grouse varies considerably, according as to whether the moor is low-lying or exposed. On the most favourable ground the birds commence to lay before March is out—if the season has been an early one—and between the 2000 and the 3000-foot levels fresh eggs of the first nesting may be found up to the second week in June.

In 1913 I knew of a bird that was just hatching out her brood as late as 13th July. It is indeed a very questionable benefit for high-nesting Grouse that an early spring should be experienced, for unusual mildness causes them to lay before the risk of damage by snow is past. To take an example : The month of April 1914 brought some of the finest weather conditions that have been experienced for many years, and certain of the Grouse on the high moors were a full month earlier than usual in nesting. But May saw a great change, and before a north-easterly wind snow was drifted heavily and fiercely across the hill-tops into their southern corries. After the storm a depth of fully three feet of closely-packed snow covered these hill slopes, causing nearly every Grouse which had commenced to brood to forsake its nest. Under such circumstances the majority of the birds produce a second clutch of eggs at a later date, only the broods reared from these second hatchings rarely exceed five in number.

But hen Grouse often remain bravely on their nests during the heaviest falls of snow, and may become asphyxiated by the absence of air beneath the closely-packed layer which envelops them. After a certain May storm a keeper on a high-lying grouse moor came across no fewer than nine Grouse dead on their nests during the course of a single morning's walk. That a hen Grouse remembers her nest, even when it is inaccessible to her for several days on account of the snow which covers it, is borne out by an instance which came to my knowledge of such a bird returning to her nest after a week's storm and then succeeding in hatching off her eggs—which, it goes without saying, she had not commenced to brood upon when the storm commenced.

The following interesting account has been given me by a well-known sportsman and naturalist. A hen Grouse had her nest on a steep hill face near his shooting lodge, and through a powerful glass the hen could be seen covering her eggs, which were eight in number. One day, on looking at the nest, my informant could see that the eggs had become displaced, and that the bird was attempting to pull them back uphill into the nest, using her chin as a lever. He thereupon climbed the hill face, to find every one of the eggs outside the nest and the bird brooding where the eggs had formerly reposed. Many deer-tracks led across the hill, and, in all probability, the bird had been disturbed hurriedly and had scattered her clutch on her precipitate departure. The eggs were now replaced and the nest built up on the downhill side. A week later, about nine o'clock in the morning, it was again noticed that two of the eggs had been in some way displaced. At two o'clock the same afternoon the nest was revisited and the eggs replaced after an absence from the nest of certainly five hours, probably longer. Notwithstanding the various vicissitudes which her future family had undergone, the eggs hatched off safely in due course.

The nest of the Grouse is always of the most primitive description, and is generally devoid of even a rudimentary lining. It is usually found amongst long heather or in the shelter of a tussock of grass. It is curious that wet and boggy ground is often chosen—perhaps the fox does not do so much of his hunting here—and I have on more than one occasion found the nest in rushes. Once I heard of a Grouse having her nest and hatching off her eggs on an island on a Highland loch. Although it has been stated that a hen Grouse will readily forsake her nest before she has commenced to brood, I do not think that this is the case, and certainly once she has begun to sit she is devoted to her eggs. A friend of mine tells me that his retriever on one occasion pulled several of the feathers out of the tail of a sitting bird without causing her to forsake her nest, and that in the course of his long experience he has only once known of a Grouse deserting her eggs, the occasion being when the bird was caught on the nest and carried some distance in his dog's mouth. A hen Grouse usually sits closely, though she does not equal the Ptarmigan in this respect, and rarely permits of a photograph of her being taken at close quarters. When disturbed she rises with much fluttering of wings and dashes out of sight, flying at great speed. She never, so far as my experience goes, returns to watch what fate befalls her eggs, nor does the cock join her in mid-air. It would thus seem as though she were lacking in courage or confidence as compared with the Tarmachan, for the latter bird as often as not refuses to move any distance from her nest, and it is the almost invariable rule that immediately she rises the cock, who has been anxiously watching events, dashes down and joins his mate in her flight.

The eggs laid by a Grouse vary considerably in number. An average clutch consists of from six to nine, but I have seen as many as eleven—and that, too, on high ground—and during the present season (1914) I hear of a Grouse sitting on no fewer than fifteen eggs. It is a most difficult thing to distinguish a Grouse's egg from that of a Ptarmigan—I doubt, indeed, whether it is possible in some cases —but, if anything, those laid by the Grouse are slightly the larger of the two. The ground colour is pale brown, and the egg is plentifully marked with dark brown or rich red-brown spots and blotches. Sometimes, when the egg has just been laid, the colouring is remarkably beautiful. At times a Grouse will produce amongst her clutch a dwarf egg. On one occasion I found such an egg scarcely larger than that of a Blackbird, and a stalker came across a nest containing an exceptionally large double-yolked egg and also a dwarf egg. Considering how cleverly concealed the nest of a Grouse usually is, it is surprising how easily a pair of Hoodies discover its whereabouts. Stoats, too, devour many of the eggs, and the Black-headed Gull also has recently acquired an unenviable reputation in this respect.

A great deal of discussion and uncertainty has existed as to what degree of frost a Grouse's egg will stand, but no definite investigations have up to the present been conducted on the subject, so far as I am aware. It is undoubtedly the case, however, that during the period when a Grouse is laying a reading of five or six degrees of frost occurs frequently during the hours of darkness, and yet the eggs suffer no injury. A few hours after hatching the young Grouse are full of life and activity. Should the weather be warm and bright at the time, the mother Grouse does not brood on them, contenting herself with watching them closely till the dipping of the sun on the horizon. In cold weather she broods them almost as closely as she did her eggs, for the chicks are very susceptible to a keen wind, and commence to shiver violently and to seek out any shelter there is handy within a few minutes of their mother leaving them. Grouse with young vary greatly in their behaviour when disturbed. The cock is usually near the hen, and both birds may fly off so unconcernedly that they might well have no children in danger. More often, however, the cock Grouse flies right away, while his mate flops and flounders over the heather in her attempt to decoy the intruder from the whereabouts of her family. Sometimes I have found it possible to call her up almost to my feet by imitating the alarm cry of a young Grouse in distress, but this ruse is not usually so successful as it is with the Ptarmigan.

The rate of growth of a young Grouse is rapid, especially if the weather be favourable. On the third day the primaries and secondaries commence to appear, and by the ninth are well developed. During the first weeks of their lives the young birds feed on insects—flies, beetles, caterpillars—later they eat heather shoots and the tender stems and leaves of the blaeberry (*Vaccinium myrtillus*). I have seen young birds strong on the wing on June 6th, at a date when some of the Grouse on the higher beats had scarcely commenced to brood. During their youth Grouse at times suffer severely from the attacks of a minute unicellular organism, by name *Eimeria avium*. This parasite is unintentionally picked up by the bird with its food or water, and destroys the intestines of its host. As this illness, or coccidiosis, as it is termed, is highly infectious, it is important that the dead chicks be burnt whenever possible. Coccidiosis, it must be borne in mind, is a malady totally distinct from the so-called Grouse disease. The latter scourge has been traced, thanks to the exertions of the Grouse Disease Committee, to a minute thread-worm, to which the imposing name of *Trichostrongylus pergracilis* has been assigned. This minute thread or round worm—the male is $\frac{1}{3}$ to $\frac{1}{4}$ inch, the female $\frac{3}{8}$ to $\frac{1}{2}$ an inch in length—is not confined to sickly Grouse alone, and the point should, I think, be emphasized that practically every Grouse on every moor harbours the parasites in larger or fewer numbers. The thread-worms take up their stations among the young leaves and flowers of the heather, where they remain till swallowed by the bird with its food, and when present in large numbers, set up acute appendicitis in their victim. It is only, however, when the Grouse on a moor become enfeebled either by injudicious burning of the ground, overstocking of the moor, or by an absence of food consequent upon a more than usually severe winter, that the attacks of the Nematodes are sufficiently virulent to affect the health of the birds. Since it has been discovered that the larval forms of *Trichostrongylus* are most prevalent on the young " food " heather, it is important that the moor should hold as much of this heather as possible, so as to give to the birds extensive feeding ground. A few words as to the heather-burning on a moor may not be out of place. The Grouse Committee are of opinion that the great majority of moors are insufficiently burnt. On most of the moors the rotation for heather-burning is not less than fifty years, which means that the amount of heather is only eighteen per cent. of the total area. In their opinion the burning of the moor on a fifteen-year rotation should be practised, for then no less than sixty per cent. of the ground would consist of heather affording good feeding for the birds. Also, when heather under the age of twenty years is burnt, the new crop usually springs from the root the following season, whereas old heather is not replaced for half a dozen years—in some cases a much longer period—for the whole of the regeneration must come from seed. Unfortunately, the heather-burning season is all too short. Unless special notice has been lodged with the sheriff of the county, the legal close of fire-raising on a moor is on 10th April, though the extension permits of burning up to the 25th. There is always a risk of destroying a certain number of eggs during late burning. It is thus permissible to suggest that more advantage be taken of the opportunities afforded of autumn burning. It is legal to light a fire any day after 1st November, and there are days in late autumn when the heather will burn cleanly and without difficulty. On a carefully-burnt moor no heather more than twelve inches in height should be found. It is also important to burn any long heather growing on the banks of burns and near springs, so as to enable the young Grouse to have access to water without difficulty.

The weight of a Grouse in perfect health and condition varies considerably. The average weight of the males may be put at one and a half pounds, the females being a few ounces lighter. The heaviest birds are said to come from Caithness and from the South of Ireland : one from the latter district turned the scales at no less than two and a half pounds.

Concerning the origin of the word " Grouse " little is known. As far back as 1531 the name is found mentioned, with the spelling " Grows " : the word in its present form—Grouse—being met with in 1603. In 1678 the naturalist Willughby calls the bird the " Gorcock " and the " Red Game." The Scottish naturalist, MacGillivray, sometimes speaks of the Grouse as the Red Ptarmigan.

The enemies of the Grouse are varied. The Eagle

and Peregrine take their toll ; the hill fox pounces upon the birds as they brood, and often one finds the hole where Reynard has temporarily deposited his victim. Great damage is done by the stealthy stoat, which has a special liking for the eggs of this moorland bird. An interesting case is on record of a Grouse having been captured and killed by an otter.

To all who know the moors the call note of the Red Grouse is familiar. A Gaelic tradition has it that when he rises excited from the heather at your feet, the cock cries out, " Cò, cò, cò, mo chlaidh, mo chlaidh," which may be interpreted as " Who goes there ? My sword, my sword." The call of the hen is a nasal " yow, yow, yow." It is comparatively seldom heard, however, and seems to be uttered chiefly during the quiet of the early morning when a hen Grouse with her brood suspects the presence of danger.

The Grouse, as is natural with so hardy a bird, is not too particular as to its food. At all seasons of the year they feed on the young shoots of the ling (*Calluna vulgaris*), and are partial to the shoots of the blaeberry. They feed on the crowberry (*Empetrum nigrum*), on the bell heather (*Erica cinerea*), on the cotton grass (*Eriophorum*), and on the bedstraw (*Galium saxatile*).

During the months of autumn they are partial to the berries of the blaeberry, to the bearberry (*Arctostaphylos*), to the two cranberries (*Vaccinium vitis idœa* and *Vaccininium occycoccus*), and to the averine or cloudberry (*Rubus chamœmorus*). They eat the blossoms of the heather, also its seeds. Insects are taken as well.

The winter's frost and snow acts as a preservative to the various berries on the higher moors, and Grouse have access to them at times till well past the New Year.

Unlike the Willow Grouse or Ptarmigan, the Red Grouse has only two moults during the year. It is also a curious fact that the cock Grouse has no moult before the nesting season ; it breeds in the plumage it has assumed at the beginning of the winter. The hen, on the other hand, has a complete summer dress before she commences incubation. It has been suggested by a well-known investigator that the moult, in the case of the male bird, has been postponed from spring to summer as a result of the attacks of the strongylus worm. After the winter the Grouse are always a more ready prey to disease, and it is possible that the attacks of the parasite and the strain on the cocks during the season of pairing and nesting has necessitated the postponement of the moult till the commencement of June.

There are so many types of Grouse in existence in these Islands that a precise description of their plumage is impossible. Sometimes on the high grounds birds are found with several of the flight feathers white, and this may well be a " throw back " or atavism to the time when the Grouse was plumaged in white during the winter, and when the flight feathers were white throughout the year. The feet and cheeks of high-nesting Grouse, too, are often white. The young, when first hatched, have the crown dark brown, bordered with a still darker colour, which extends in a line across the forehead to the base of the bill, and in a wide band down the back of the neck. The upper parts are prettily mottled with several shades of colour. The cheeks and throat are of pale yellow.

The Red Grouse occasionally crosses with the Black Grouse, and handsome hybrids result. As I mentioned earlier, apparent hybrids between Grouse and Ptarmigan have been obtained, but they have never been entirely above suspicion.

Though the Grouse is a bird peculiar to Great Britain,

it has been introduced, and is now thriving, on a high tract of moorland between Belgium and Germany.

On the Shetlands it was set down as an experiment in 1858. The birds lingered till 1872, but the district was for some reason unfavourable, and they became extinct about the latter date.

THE CAPERCAILLIE

TETRAO UROGALLUS

CAPULL-COILLE (*Gaelic*); AUERHAHN (*German*); GLUDAR (*Russian*).

CONCERNING the derivation of the Gaelic word Capercaillie not a little doubt exists. By some it is suggested that the word should read Cabharcoille, which would signify, " The Old Bird of the Woods." Others say that the word may be derived from Gabharcoille, " The Goat of the Woods," in allusion to the long feathers on the throat of the male. I am inclined to believe that the latter interpretation is the more likely of the two. The history of the Capercaillie in Scotland is an interesting one. In former times, when the great Caledonian forest covered hundreds of thousands of acres, the bird was found through a wide extent of the country, but owing to various causes—chiefly, I believe, to the destruction of the ancient woodlands—had become extinct by the second half of the eighteenth century. In 1827 a number of Capercaillie were brought across from Sweden, and were liberated at Mar Lodge, on the upper reaches of the Dee. This attempt at introduction was a failure, however, but a second effort, made ten years later at Taymouth, was entirely successful. From Perthshire the Capercaillie has spread over a large extent of Scotland. In Aberdeenshire it is numerous in localities favourable to its habits, and is found also in the counties of Elgin, Nairn, Inverness, Ross and Cromarty.

The favourite haunt of the Capercaillie is a forest of Scots pines aged from eighty to a hundred years. Trees of this advanced age are, I think, preferred to younger plantations, probably because there is an absence of undergrowth which would impede the birds in their movements. I have never seen them in a birch wood.

The nest of the Capercaillie is placed on the ground at the foot of a tree, often a tree which has grown in a curve, and which thus protects the sitting hen from the wet, being preferred. The eggs usually number from six to nine, but as many as twelve have been found. During the period of laying the hen bird covers them roughly with pine needles on her departure from the nest. In colour they are of a pale brownish buff ground colour, spotted lightly with reddish brown. They resemble those of the Grey-hen, but are more handsome in appearance and of larger size. An average measurement is 2·2 by 1·6 inches. Sometimes two hens share the same nest. The Capercaillie is a somewhat late nester, and the majority are still brooding on eggs during the first weeks in June. The period of incubation is just over four weeks. At times a hen Capercaillie will brood so closely that one can approach to within a few feet without causing her to leave the nest. She cannot, however, be said to be a good mother, and seems to be contented if only a few of her young follow her from the nest. It is probable, however, that individual birds vary greatly in their affection for their young, for I knew of one instance when, on a brood of young Capers being disturbed, the mother bird flew up and endeavoured to beat off the human intruder.

When disturbed on her nest, the departure of the hen Capercaillie is a precipitate one, and she often carries with her one or more of the eggs. These remain where they have fallen, perhaps only an inch outside the nest, for the bird, as far as my experience goes, makes no attempt to replace them. Stoats remove the eggs from the nest, and I have more than once seen a deserted nest with the sucked eggs lying around. On one occasion some mysterious marauder gradually removed all the eggs from a nest, in spite of the fact that the bird was in possession.

It would indeed seem that in all birds which are polygamous in their habits the parental instinct is not so firmly planted as in those which remain constant to one mate throughout the nesting season. During the pairing season the Capercaillies hold a kind of " Lek " or courting at break of day, and again, but less frequently, in the evening. A male bird takes up his station on one of the upper branches of a pine, and by his display attracts a number of hens to the vicinity. The song of the male Capercaillie commences with a number of clucking cries, repeated at intervals of a second or two, then comes a cry which may be compared to the drawing of the cork from a bottle, and finally a " swishing " note. It is during this last effort that the singer closes his eyes, shakes his head, and is forgetful of everything, save his own display, for the time being. Should a rival cock appear on the scene at such a time, a fierce combat ensues until the vanquished is either driven from the scene or is left dead on the battle-field.

In most European countries the Capercaillie is stalked during his " display," and the sport is full of incident and calls for a considerable amount of skill and wariness. The stalker makes his way into the heart of the forest before dawn, armed, perhaps, with a lantern, and, having discovered a spot frequented by the birds, he extinguishes his light and sits himself down to await events. As the first streaks of dawn become visible in the east, the clucking calls of a Capercaillie are heard proceeding from a tree near, and the stalk is commenced. It is a slow business, as forward progress is possible only when the bird is engaged in uttering the last part of his love song, and even then there is time only for an advance of three or four paces. During the intervals between their singing the

Capercaillies are always on the alert, and the snapping of even a small twig will send them from their perch in precipitate flight. Long before sunrise the Capercaillies are silent once more, and then the loud clear notes of the Missel Thrush break the early morning stillness. These daybreak scenes in the big forests have an especial charm to the nature-lover. Gradually the sun rises and throws soft rosy rays on the western hills, lighting up the pines in their corries and tinging their lingering snowfields with its beams.

For a bird so large and heavy—the male bird weighs twelve pounds—the flight of the Capercaillie is certainly skilful. They are able to speed through a thick wood at a speed approaching a mile a minute, and yet can avoid trees and branches of trees with sudden and masterly swerves. It is said that after a period of wet and stormy weather their plumage becomes saturated to such an extent that they are unable to rise from the ground. Sometimes in autumn Capercaillie leave the shelter of their forests and pay visits to the cornfields near, to feed on the grain. The damage done by them, however, is insignificant compared to that worked by the Black-cock. Though usually a shy and retiring bird, an instance is on record of a cock Capercaillie attacking with great fierceness any person venturing to pass through that part of the forest where he dwelt. The usual food of the Capercaillie consists of pine needles, young and tender shoots being taken. The damage caused by them in older woods is slight, but in young plantations of pine and larch they destroy the leaders of the trees. They feed on insects and their larvæ, and in autumn eat various wild fruits. It is said that the hens, with their young broods, consume large numbers of pupæ of the ant. It has certainly been my experience that favourite nesting sites of the Capercaillie are usually plentiful in ant-heaps—some

of great size and several feet in height—and I have seen
these mounds scattered about, in all probability by Capercaillies.   During dry weather the birds are fond of re-
sorting to the stalking paths and roads intersecting a
forest for the purpose of indulging in dust-baths.   On
account of their pine diet the flesh of the Capercaillie
is bitter and resinous, but young birds of the year are
sometimes eaten.

So early as 1617 the Capercaillie would seem to have
been scarce in Scotland.   In a letter written by James VI
to Lord Tullibardine, the king mentions that "the rarity
of these fowles will make their estimation the more pre-
tious."

Outside Scotland the range of the Capercaillie is a
wide one.   It is numerous in the pine forests of Russia
and Germany, where the stalking of the birds during the
pairing season provides good sport.   In Scandinavia it
is found as far north as latitude 70 degrees.   Eastward
it is met with as far as Lake Baikal.   It nests in the
Pyrenees, Alps, Carpathians, and the Altai Mountains.
In the Ural Mountains an allied form, *Tetrus uralensis*,
takes its place.   This sub-species is noticeably paler than
our own form.

Other sub-species are found in North-East Siberia
and Kamschatka.

Description : Male.—Head and neck dark grey,
mottled with black.   Throat with greenish tinge.   Mantle,
lower back, and rump black, with white lines appearing
at intervals.   Inter-scapular region marked with reddish-
brown.   Wing coverts brown, spotted with black.   Quills
and primary coverts dark brown.   Chest glossy green,
merging to black on the breast and abdomen, some of
the feathers being white-tipped.   Thighs white.   Leg
feathers dark brown.   Tail black, with white band across
the terminal half of the feathers.   Axillaries and under

wing coverts white. Bill yellow. Feet dark grey.
Wattle scarlet. Length, 35 inches; wing, 14·6 inches;
tail, 12·3 inches; tarsus, 2·8 inches.

Female.—Head, neck, and upper parts, wing coverts
and secondaries black, barred with reddish-brown and
tipped with white except on the back. Primaries dark
brown. Throat, fore-neck, and under parts rufous buff.
Tail brown, barred with black and tipped with white.
Axillaries and under wing coverts white marked with
brown and black. Bill brownish. Feet grey brown.
Total length about 25 inches; wing, 11·7 inches; tail, 7·3
inches; tarsus, 2·1 inches.

Barren females not infrequently assume male plumage.
The young when hatched have the top of the head buff,
mottled with black, and with a dark V-shaped mark on
the forehead. A black band is found behind the eyes,
and extends to the sides of the neck. Nape, wing coverts,
and rump fawn colour. Back mottled with grey-brown.
Throat light yellow.

THE WOODCOCK

SCOLOPAX RUSTICOLA

COILEACH-COILLE, CROM-NAN-DUILLEAG CREÒTHAR (*Gaelic*); BÉCASSE (*French*); WALDSCHNEPPE (*German*). Local names :—MUFF COCK, MUCKLE SNIPPACK.

To those who know the wooded glens of the Highlands during the months of April and May the Woodcock compels attention from its curious and distinctive habit of emerging from the obscurity in which it has hidden itself during the day and flying over the tree-tops with rapid, trembling wing-beats. To this behaviour the Scandinavians have given the term " Rôding," and, as in our own language there is, so far as I am aware, no distinctive name in use, I think it may be as well to keep to it throughout this chapter. Immediately after sunset the entire male Woodcock population leave their secluded haunts and fly backwards and forwards over the same line of country, uttering a peculiar cry, unheard except during the season of nesting. The notes may be termed the song of the males, and are uttered by the birds previous to their departure for their feeding-grounds in the evening. The song commences with grunting cries, ending up with a sharp and penetrating note repeated, maybe several times in quick succession, " pisick, pisick." At times two cock birds during their aerial manœuvres cross one another's path, and then ensues a stern chase over the tree-tops, the birds uttering repeatedly their chirping cries. The " rôding " of the Woodcock never takes place before the sun has set during the earlier part of spring, but at a more advanced period —in May—the birds commence their evening flights

rather earlier. The flighting is continued till deep twilight
has settled over the glen, but ceases before night. In the
morning I, personally, have never heard this "rôding,"
but it is said to be recommenced before daybreak, and
to cease previous to full daylight. The Woodcock when
rôding does not fly repeatedly over the same part of the
wood ; there is an interval between each of its appearances.

It is said to pass over the same country three times in
the course of the evening. On the first visit it flies high and
usually fast ; on the second, its progress is lower and more
leisurely, while on the third and last the bird moves just
above the trees. This habit of the Woodcock is an unfortunate one, did the bird but know it, for on the Continent
—in France, Germany, and other countries—sportsmen go
out just before sunset and conceal themselves on the
ground over which the Woodcock are in the habit of
rôding. In Scandinavia large numbers are shot in this
way ; in Sweden the line of country traversed by them
is known as the "drag " or " sträck." In Germany and in
Scandinavia the Woodcock are supposed to make their
first appearance on the third Sunday in Lent, which is
called Woodcock Sunday. An old sporting rhyme fixes
the arrival and the departure of the birds as follows :

> " Oculi da kommen sie
> Lactare, das hahre
> Judica, sind sie auch noch da.
> Palmarum, trallarum."

With Palm Sunday the migration ceases.

The well-known sportsman, St. John, writing more
than half a century ago, gave it as his opinion that the
Woodcock was the first of all Highland birds to commence
nesting. Though this is scarcely correct—the Raven is
brooding before February is out, and the Heron a few
days later—the Woodcock is undoubtedly one of the
earliest birds to breed. By the third week in March the

earlier individuals are brooding, and by the first week in April nesting is general. The nesting ground is usually a wood, deciduous trees being, I think, preferred, owing to the soft layer of fallen leaves covering the ground. Close-grown plantations are rarely chosen as nesting sites, and small belts of birch and oak are favourite nesting grounds, provided that there is plenty of space between the trees. It is my experience that the birds dislike dense cover in which to nest ; a few broken-down bracken offer a suitable position, or the bird may scrape out a hollow amongst the deep layers of fallen beech and oak leaves which cover the ground beneath these trees. The eggs usually number four, but at times only three are found. Their ground colour is normally buff coloured, and they are liberally spotted and blotched by dark reddish-brown markings. Nothing more primitive than the nest of the Woodcock can be found in the bird world. It is merely a slight hollow scraped in the ground and generally without intentional lining of any kind. The mother Woodcock often sits very hard on her eggs, especially if incubation be far advanced, for she relies on the close harmonisation of her plumage with her surroundings. Sometimes I have been able to approach to within a few feet of such a bird, and by not the slightest movement did she betray that she was alive. As the result of her early nesting, the Woodcock has sometimes to cover her eggs when snow lies around to a considerable depth.

The young, as is the case with " waders " generally, are able to move about a short time after hatching. They are buff in colour, with a reddish chocolate median band extending along the back to the crown, where it branches and runs forward over the eyes.

Although such an early nester, I have seen eggs of the Woodcock as late as the third week in July, which seems to point to the fact that in certain instances two broods are reared in the course of a season. It is worth noting that prior to the nineteenth century no case of Woodcock nesting in Britain was recorded. It is unlikely that the birds have changed their habits since then ; more probably an increased interest in nature study has revealed their presence in localities where they formerly nested in obscurity. The Woodcock is remarkable amongst birds in that it carries its young considerable distances in order to remove them from a danger zone. If a bird be disturbed suddenly with her brood around her, she sometimes snatches up the chick which happens to be nearest to her and carries it off, holding it apparently between her legs. On a certain occasion a stalker surprised such a bird on the bank of a river, and, picking up one of her brood, she bore it over to the farther side, to return, presumably, with her travelled child after the danger had passed. This remarkable habit of the Woodcock is one which has been noted by so many and accurate observers that it is somewhat surprising it is still regarded with scepticism by certain ornithologists. Such, nevertheless is the case, and every time the statement appears in print a sheaf of letters are forthcoming from those who seek to cast doubts on the narrative of the observer who witnessed the event. On the other hand, certain writers of repute indeed go so far as to assert that the young Woodcock are carried to the feeding-grounds by their parents nightly.

During its flight the bill of the Woodcock is pointed downwards, and the wings are not extended to their full stretch. It seldom makes sustained flights, however, except on migration. During a shoot at Alnwick a Woodcock was seen to alight on the ground and then to throw leaves over its back, presumably to hide itself from the guns. If so, it would seem that the Woodcock is one of the most sagacious of birds. It feeds mainly by night on wet, boggy ground, and eats an enormous quantity of worms ; indeed, it may swallow almost its own weight of food in the course of a single day. When the blaeberries have ripened, the Woodcock betake themselves to the hillsides and consume great quantities of the fruit. At the present time Woodcock are plentiful in Scotland during the months of spring and summer, and even south of the Border nest in many suitable localities. It is probable that the birds nesting in these Islands do not remain with us through the winter, and that their place is taken by migrants from the north. During the winter the Mediterranean basin is the resort of great numbers of Woodcock. These quarters it reaches in early November, and leaves as soon as February, passing through Germany and the British Isles in March or early in April. The return migration takes place mainly in October. Many of the birds cross the North Sea and arrive along the eastern Scottish coasts. They remain here only a short time, and continue their flight westward. Some halt on the western seaboard of Scotland, others continue their way into Ireland, where they remain through the winter. The principal summer home of the Woodcock is the northern portion of the Old World, for it is found extending from Eastern Siberia to the western extremity of Europe. The Woodcock nesting in Kamschatka migrate to Japan with the advent of the cold weather, those frequenting Mongolia to China, while those which have nested in Western Siberia and on the plateau of Thibet move down to Burmah, India, Afghanistan, and Persia. Our own winter visitors are those birds which have bred in Scandinavia, Finland, and perhaps Russia. Those which press on south past our Islands arrive in Palestine, in North Africa, and in Egypt. Throughout Russia the Woodcock is found nesting, extending, though in diminished numbers, as far south as the Caucasus and the Crimea. It also breeds in Central France and in Northern Italy. Some of its most distant nesting grounds are in Kashmir and Japan, while it has been found breeding in the Himalayas at the height of 10,000 feet. In the Faroe Islands it has occurred as a passing visitor, and has also been recorded from Spitzbergen.

Description.—The sexes resemble each other, and there is no marked nesting plumage. Forehead and crown brownish grey. Back of head crossed by four bars of dark brown, divided by bands of buff. Lores marked by narrow band of dark brown, and a band is also below the eyes. Back of the neck brownish grey, with black sides. Throat white, bounded by a brown and black band. Wings and wing coverts chestnut, barred conspicuously with black. Lowermost rows of minor coverts, median and major coverts tipped with buff, forming distinct transverse bars. Major coverts and secondaries crossed by broad bands of black. Primaries dark grey with white tips. Rump and tail coverts chestnut, barred with black. Tail feathers black, tipped above with silver grey and below with white. Breast and abdomen light brown, barred with narrow lines, under tail coverts brown with markings of black. The mature young cannot be distinguished from its parents.

THE SNIPE

SCOLOPAX GALLINAGO

Gaelic names :—Butagochd, Meannan-adhair, Eun-ghabhrag, Gabhar-adhair, Croman lòin ; Bécassine ordinaire (*French*) ; Moor-schneppe (*German*). Local names :—Moor or Mire Snipe, Heather Bleater, Full Snipe, Single Snipe, Snippack, Gowk, House Gowk.

To this small wader are assigned in the Gaelic language a number of imposing names : *Meannan-adhair* signifies the " Small kid of the air," and a somewhat similar meaning lies in *Gabhar-adhair*. *Croman lòin*, again, has reference to the peculiar flight of the Snipe, for it may be translated as the " Small crooked creature of the marsh."

The most interesting point in the natural history of the Snipe is its peculiar, one might almost say unique, habit of " drumming " during the nesting season. Both sexes are said to indulge in this " drumming," but, personally, I think that the cock is the more regular and proficient performer, and that his evolutions are for the benefit of his mate, resembling in this respect the spring song of the Lapwing, or the slow soaring flight of the Golden Plover. For long the precise location of this bleating sound remained undecided—even at the present day all naturalists are not agreed on the matter—but it is generally conceded that it has its origin from the rush of wind acting on the stiff external tail feathers as the bird descends rapidly. Formerly it was believed that the wings of the bird produced the curious sound, and Mac-Gillivray puts forward the statement that " from the rapid beats of his wing the tremulous air gives to the ear what at first seems the voice of distant thunder." It is only during the spring and early summer months that the Snipe drums, and one rarely hears him before April. On still evenings of early summer it is good to wander into the country of the Heather Bleater, and listen to the birds as they wing their way backward and forward overhead above a favourite nesting site of theirs. But one rarely hears them during the hours of sunshine and heat : one must needs go down to their bog toward sunset. On one occasion I made my way down the river banks as the sun was low in the west, to a certain stretch of marsh land where Snipe are always to be found. From a field of tussocky grass several Redshank sprang on my approach, crossing the river with excited whistlings, but as yet, the season was too young to find their eggs. Many Lapwings, too, were near the river, and a Heron, interrupted in his fishing, made his way clumsily to a more secluded spot. As I reached the big marsh the air was quiet, but gradually, as the mists rolled in from the coast and the sun became dim and fiery red in colour, there rose from the bog, not one, but several Snipe. At top speed they dashed backwards and forwards with rapid wing-beats. Every now and again a bird would descend slantingly earthwards, turning rather over on his side and producing the characteristic bleating sound. After a couple of seconds or so the bird checked his dipping, and at once the sound ceased. Anything more rapid than the wing-beats of a Snipe during this characteristic flight cannot be imagined, and after a time the birds, one after the other, dipped down into the rushes at express speed. One particular individual I noted possessing a " bleat " unlike his fellows. The key was abnormally low, and the bird, too, appeared to be larger than average size. Many Curlews crossed over the country of the Snipe as I lay there, their trilling whistles echoing across the glen, and

remained hidden, and we thought she had gone there to shelter, but presently she emerged from her obscurity, and following her closely were two small chicks. By comparison with the green grass these little people appeared almost black, so dark was their downy plumage. Their mother realised that danger was near, for she led them quickly away, but never turned to see whether her children were following her. They kept their position close behind her, although the pace for them was a quick one, and they were soon lost to sight behind a ridge. One realised how wonderfully obedient the chicks were : they were left in the rushes at the approach of danger, their mother having evidently enjoined them to remain concealed and without movement until she returned for them. A little later on we again came upon the family party : they were feeding in a grass-covered ditch, and at our approach the parent rose and flew off as though she had no young near. Once she soared characteristically, dipping until she had almost touched the ground before she moved her wings to drive her forward.

Although eminent authorities have stated that a Snipe with a brood by her feigns lameness to distract attention, I have never found this to be the case, the bird invariably flying off as she does when sitting on her eggs. The young Snipe have the bill long almost from the first. They are clad in down of a dark brownish red colour, and are spotted with dusky brown about the head and on their upper parts.

Although the Snipe is generally distributed throughout the glens of the Highlands; it is rarely found nesting at high altitudes. In the Forest of Gaick, where the eggs are not infrequently taken by blackheaded gulls, it breeds plentifully at an altitude of 1500 feet above sea-level, and it also nests near Loch Eunach, among the Cairngorms, at a height of close on 2000 feet. During the winter months great flights of these birds arrive on our coasts from Norway and Sweden, but it is said that even during migration these Snipe never travel in flocks, but always either singly or in pairs. In its feeding habits the Snipe is nocturnal. Its food consists of worms, insects, and also of delicate plant roots. It is supposed to be able to swallow the morsel without withdrawing its bill from the soft ground. To the northward of Scotland the Snipe has a wide range. In the Faroes it is found nesting, and in Iceland it is fairly plentiful. In Scandinavia and in Denmark it is common. It extends its range considerably beyond the Arctic Circle, and is found in most of the northern districts of Russia. At the approach of winter many Snipe migrate south to the Mediterranean region and along the Red Sea. From here they make their way through Persia and India, and are found also in Ceylon Burmah, China, and Japan. The Jack Snipe, which is found in Great Britain during the months of winter, is held not to nest in these Islands, though I hear that in 1914 an authenticated case of its nesting in Sutherland is on record.

Description.—The bird may be distinguished from the Great Snipe by the tawny, rufous colour of its outer tail feathers. The tail feathers usually number from fourteen to sixteen, but sometimes only twelve. The crown of the head is marked by a median and two lateral lines of buff. Lores dark brown. Back and sides of the neck buff, lined with dark brown. Interscapulars and scapulars black, edged with yellow. The feathers along the outer border of interscapulars have the outer web rich buff forming a conspicuous longitudinal band. Wing coverts dark brownish grey tipped with white and buff. Major coverts and secondaries dark grey narrowly tipped with white. Primaries dark grey. Tail feathers have basal portion black, succeeded by a yellow band. There is a sub-terminal band of black and terminal

band of white. Breast, flanks, and abdomen white. The
flanks may be barred with dark grey. Under tail coverts
pale brown barred with black. Bill brown. Legs greenish olive. The full fledged young lack the longitudinal
stripes on the back, which is black; marked with lines of
buffish white and dark chestnut. The forehead is pale
brown barred with black—the flanks also. There is no
seasonal change in colouration with the Snipe, and the
sexes are alike. The length of the male Snipe is 10¾
inches, and the extent of the wings 16 inches. The female
is rather larger, being 11¼ inches long, and the wing expanse 17¼ inches.

THE GOOSANDER

MERGUS MERGANSER

Iach Fhiacailleach (*Gaelic*); Grand-harle (*French*); Grosser Säger (*German*). Local names :—Sawbill, Saw-neb, Dun-diver.

It is a debatable point whether certain of our Highland birds have extended their breeding range farther south during the last half century, or whether, with the growth of interest in ornithology, more interest in the nesting of these birds is now taken than was formerly the case, and so fresh discoveries are being brought to light. Be that as it may, it is an undoubted fact that more than one bird which was formerly quite unknown as a nesting species in Great Britain is now found regularly in certain localities. The Goosander is a case in point. The first record of its nesting in Scotland was obtained so recently as in 1871 from Perthshire, while now (1914) it is by no means a rare bird north of the Tay during the months of spring and summer, and is looked on with scant favour by fishermen on account of the large number of young trout and salmon which it consumes—so much so that it has recently been in several districts removed from the lists of those birds protected by law.

The Goosander is such a handsome bird that its extermination would be a most regrettable occurrence, still I am bound to say that the damage worked by a pair of these birds amongst the trout of a hill burn is extensive. Not long ago I had occasion to traverse one of these burns for a considerable distance. The district was one of the wildest in Scotland, with not a single croft visible as far as the eye could reach, so that the birds would be left undisturbed year after year. Near the head of the burn trout were extremely abundant, every pool being crowded with fish of various sizes, but gradually I noticed that the trout became less numerous until scarcely a single individual could be made out even in the most likely pools. The white droppings of a Goosander on his favourite stone, and a sight of both birds as they rose in front of me and winged their way rapidly down stream, at once explained the scarcity of fish at that part of the burn. A short time before this occurrence, I had been told by a veteran watcher on a neighbouring deer forest, that every trout on his beat had been eaten up by a pair of Goosanders, and after my own experience I am inclined to attach a good deal of truth to his statement.

In its habits, as in its appearance, the Goosander resembles its ally, the Red-Breasted Merganser, so much so that the two birds are often confused—and, indeed, even the name, Red-Breasted Merganser, is almost unknown in some parts of the Highlands where the birds themselves are not uncommon. As a general rule, it is true, the Goosander is the larger bird, but the Merganser varies considerably in size. Especially close is the resemblance between the hen birds of the two species, and only a near view of the hen can place her identity beyond dispute.

But in their nesting habits there is considerable difference. The Merganser is, perhaps, the latest of all the ducks to commence to brood, for June has arrived before her clutch is completed, whereas the Goosander may be sitting tight as early as April 4th. The nests of the two species can always be identified at once by the down on which the eggs rest. The down of the Goosander is of a creamy yellow throughout, whereas that of the Merganser is light grey with a bluish tinge, the centres being almost white, and the tips greyish white. The Merganser,

too, is not so essentially a bird of the hills as the Goosander,
for it may be found nesting along the shores of broad rivers
in the Lowlands, whereas the Goosander is confined to the
true Highlands.

Considering the exposed nature of the ground where
it breeds, the Goosander is an early nester. Before March
is out the first eggs are laid, and the young are hatched
before the Merganser has commenced to brood. The
nesting station of the Goosander is usually a hollow in
some very old tree, and the nest may be at a considerable distance from water. Sometimes it is placed in
a crevice of a rock, or in a hollow amongst large stones.
A recent expedition I made to a nesting site of the Goosander resulted in the discovery of a hen bird sitting
hard in the hollow of an old Scots pine. It may be mentioned that this tree is one of the most resistant to decay,
and it is rare indeed to find a specimen containing a hole
of sufficient size to suit the requirements of a lady Goosander, so that when such a hollow is discovered it is almost
certain to be tenanted. The nesting site in this particular
instance was in a forest of Scots pines about 1200 feet
above sea-level. A couple of evenings before, an ornithologist companion and I had seen a particularly handsome Goosander drake feeding on the shallows of the
river a few miles lower down, and we learned from a
neighbouring stalker that the previous season a Goosander
had nested in a hollow tree in the forest above.

The day of the expedition was in early May, and in
the clear atmosphere all the hills were most sharply defined.
On the high peak of Loch-na-gar the sun shone brightly,
lighting up the great snowfields on its north-facing slopes.
Nearer at hand the Glen of the Golden Eagle was in dark,
deep shadow, while away to the nor'west a great inky
black cloud was gathering about Beinn a' Bhuird, the
whole hill being soon blotted out in a storm of rain and

hail. For some time we searched the fir wood without success, and then, on rounding a specially large hollow pine, became aware of repeated hissing cries emerging from the interior, from which a hen Goosander regarded us furiously. Though trembling with fear and anger, she refused to leave the nest until a hand was thrust into the hollow. From the photograph of the nesting site it will be seen that the entrance to the hole becomes considerably narrower near the ground, so that it was impossible for the mother bird to make her way out without flying perpendicularly up the hole for some feet. We had an opportunity of admiring her beautiful plumage as she sat there guarding her eggs. Her rich chocolate-coloured head she constantly moved from side to side in her anxiety, and her back, with its pearl-grey feathers, was trembling and quivering.

After a certain amount of gentle persuasion the Goosander left her eggs, and attempted to fly out of the nesting hollow. She almost reached the top, but failed to secure a foothold and fell back on to her eggs, unfortunately cracking one as she did so. Again she made the attempt, and with the help of my companion, who thrust a hand under her just as she was on the point of slipping back once more, gained the open and flew rapidly down the glen, quacking huskily. In the nest were eight cream-coloured eggs, resting on a layer of down of like shade, but from all appearances the hen had been sitting only a few days, so that the down was not so deep as would have been the case had incubation been far advanced.

This down is plucked by the brooding Goosander from her own breast, and serves as a blanket when she is away feeding—for, as is the case with so many members of the Duck family, the drakes take but little interest in the affairs of their wives, and thus the duck has to look after herself. When she leaves the nest she covers her eggs over with the down, and the heat is thus retained for several hours. This is of special value, since the ducks feed mainly in the evening, when the air is cool, and when the eggs would otherwise rapidly lose their warmth. In the case of the nest described above, the Goosander chicks would be able to leave the nest on their own small feet, but sometimes this is quite impossible. For instance, I was recently informed by a stalker that he found a nest in a hollow tree that had no entrance except from above, and, as baby Goosanders could not be expected to clamber up the perpendicular side of a tree, the inference to be drawn is that the chicks are carried out by their mother. Sometimes, too, a Goosander chooses as a nesting site a ledge on a rock from where there is a drop of many yards to the ground below. In such a situation it would be, obviously, impossible for newly-hatched ducklings to reach the ground of their own accord.

I know a certain rocky gorge bounding the course of a hill burn where a pair of Goosanders nest every year. A mile up the glen is the Loch of the Willow—the Loch an t' Seilich of the Gael—and it is on this loch that the Goosander does the most of her fishing. On the one side the gorge is of considerable height, and it is usually here, on a ledge of rock, that the Goosander duck makes her nest. This year (1914) she decided to try the opposite side, and laid her ten eggs in a hollow among large stones not far from the water's edge.

It was an unfortunate choice on her part. May was not many days old when a great storm visited the hills. For two days rain fell heavily and steadily, and on the evening of the second day this rain changed to snow. The burn rose rapidly, for the loch at the head of the glen was filled to the brim and still the corries ran water. Nearer and nearer to the nest the waters approached, until at length the Goosander moved out into the storm, abandoning her nest to the floods. On more than one occasion a few weeks afterwards I had seen the bird restlessly winging her way backward and forward past the old nesting site, and, although I had every reason to believe that she was brooding on a second clutch of eggs, I was unable to locate the site. One evening—it was the 6th of June—my host and I made a last expedition to the nesting ground, though, after previous unsuccessful visits, we had little hope of discovering the eggs. For some time we searched, but saw no signs of the Goosander, and had almost given up our quest when, as a last resource, we climbed to the highest point of the rock and dropped a couple of stones into the burn thirty feet below us. Immediately the hen Goosander was seen flying quickly up stream, moving only a few feet above the surface of the water, and now there began a stern search for her treasures that she had been so reluctant to quit. Over perilously narrow ledges we clambered with imminent danger of falling into the burn beneath, but the elusive nest was nowhere to be seen. Soon we had searched the whole face of the rock with the exception of one hollow, guarded by blaeberry plants of a delicate green and situated about twelve feet above the water's level. A solitary and insignificant little feather, entangled amongst the vegetation, gave us fresh hope, and we determined to investigate what the elusive hollow contained. The rock below the hollow was perpendicular—overhanging even—and although, by using alarmingly small niches as footholds, I succeeded in reaching a point two feet below the hollow, farther ascent was impossible. The only thing to do was to break down a portion of the rock to create an artificially formed ledge, and after an hour's strenuous work, during which we were half blinded with the dust from the splintered rock, we succeeded in dislodging a portion, and then the writer managed to raise himself to the required level. To his intense gratification, there was the nest, containing six beautiful eggs of a pale creamy tinge, reposing on a thick layer of creamy down.

For some time there had been no appearance of the Goosander, but now she anxiously crossed and recrossed the gorge, during her last flight bringing with her a couple of her tribe, attracted either from sympathy or from curiosity, to see for themselves the cause of her anxiety. Up stream the loch narrows at its tail end, and the burn commences its course with a pool of great depth, known locally as the Black Pool. Here our Goosander halted, and, dipping down to the water's surface, swam suspiciously about, her brown head moving expectantly from side to side as she watched and waited for the moment when she could with safety return to her nest. A little later on the mother Goosander carried her young, one at a time, down to the water's edge, and led them by degrees up the burn to the Loch of the Willow. Here she gradually instilled into them the art of catching the rapid moving trout or the rose-tinted char, or she perhaps—if her brood became wearied—took them on her back and swam quietly around while her little ones dried themselves in the strong June sunlight. Not till summer has left the hills, and the birches fringing the loch have shed the very last of their golden leaves, will the Goosander leave the Loch of the Willow. Their course will lead them south'ard, for the hill loch will soon be in the grip of the ice, and not till they have, maybe, reached the waters of some English lake will they descend, and here take up their quarters for the winter.

Even when quite babies, the young of the Goosander are perfectly at home on the water. They can dive well, and remain a considerable time below the surface. They can also swim almost entirely submerged, only the top of the head showing, and the small swimmer appearing for all the world like a rat, as it makes its way as speedily as possible from the danger zone.

I think that, when danger is perceived by the mother Goosander from afar, she sees her chicks safely concealed, and rises from the water, flying backward and forward near the spot. I once saw a Goosander after behaving in this manner rise to a great height, and make her way rapidly in the direction of a neighbouring loch. On passing a certain loch where I knew at least one brood of Goosanders was concealed, I saw the Goosander duck flying around restlessly. A strong breeze was blowing down the glen at the time, rippling the clear waters of the loch, and aided by this wind the Goosander rose up, with each circle which she executed, till she had reached a great height. A pair of Eagles had their eyrie on a rock near—I had only a few minutes before seen both birds alight at their eyrie and commence to feed their hungry Eaglet—and I wondered whether the Goosander would be sighted and pursued, but no, she moved rapidly southward—making, apparently, for a loch which lay farther up the glen—until she was lost to view in the bright sky.

Sometimes very large broods of young Goosanders are seen. An angler, to whom the Highland glens are well known, on one occasion came across a family of no fewer than fourteen youngsters. On the water with them was only a single adult bird, though a second was seen in the air : whether this was the drake, or whether two broods were present and the more timid of the mothers declined to stay with her young, is doubtful.

Even in the south the Goosander at times is driven from still water by stress of weather, and then the birds frequent rivers or, perhaps, the sea itself.

One winter's afternoon I was watching the ducks on a certain loch feeding on a narrow strip of water which had so far escaped the frost. Amongst their number was a Goosander drake, conspicuously handsome in his dark and rich cream-coloured plumage. This bird dived repeatedly below the surface. For a time he was unsuccessful, but at length emerged holding in his bill a good-sized pike, which he had considerable difficulty in swallowing. Even then the fish apparently continued its struggles in its captor's interior, for he swam uneasily about until the pike had ceased fighting, when he clambered up on to the ice and stood there, in sleepy content, while he digested his well-earned meal. On one occasion an eel no less than eighteen inches in length was taken from the gullet of a Goosander duck.

The courtship and display of the Goosander has many points in common with that of the Eider drake. The bird swims in company with the ducks, and from time to time suddenly stretches his head upwards, the neck being extended and the bill gaping. At other times the bird raises the fore-part of its body in the water and bends his head low. Sometimes he jerks himself along the water, throwing up clouds of spray in the process. This courtship display is accompanied by a soft and low quacking.

The range of the Goosander is a wide one to the north of Scotland, though south of the Tweed it is unknown during the nesting season. In Iceland it breeds, and probably in Greenland also. In Norway and Sweden it is plentiful. In Lapland the eggs are taken by the peasants. Here the season of spring is late in arriving, and it is June before the birds commence to brood. In order to induce a passing Goosander to nest, the Lap places against the trunk of a pine a decayed trunk with a hole in the centre. As a hollow pine is none too common, the duck gladly avails herself of this nesting site, and the peasant, appearing periodically on the scene, removes the eggs with the exception of one, which he leaves in

M

order to induce the unfortunate bird to provide him with a further batch. In Finland and in Northern Russia the Goosander is a common summer visitor.

On the great hills of Asia it nests at the height of 10,000 feet. In India it nests amongst the Himalayas.

At the approach of autumn the Goosander migrates southward, its powerful wings enabling it to make long and sustained flights. It makes its way in search of warmth and sunlight to the southern districts of Spain and to Northern Africa. At times it is found along the Mediterranean, and in the Black Sea is fairly numerous. Eastward it is found across Siberia and Central Asia, visiting Japan and China at the close of the nesting season. In North America it is represented by a sub-species— *Mergus merganser americanus*. In winter these birds range south to the Gulf of Mexico.

Description : Male.—Head and upper part of neck black, glossed with green. Inner scapulars black, outer white. Lower back ash grey. Wing coverts white, secondaries narrowly margined with black. The lower parts of the neck, and under parts, white, the latter during the life of the bird bearing a delicate tinge of pink. Bill and iris red. Legs and feet orange red.

Later in the summer, in his eclipse plumage, the drake differs from the duck in his darker back and by having a ring of black round his neck. The Goosander duck has the head and neck bright chestnut, the red brown contrasting strongly with her white throat. Her upper parts are of a pearl grey. Major coverts broadly tipped with white, with a dusky spot on the inner web. Inner secondaries white. Under parts white except the flanks, which are barred with grey. The young when hatched are of a dark brown colour.

THE CURLEW

NUMENIUS ARQUATUS

GUILBNEACH, GUILBINN (*Gaelic*).
"Coire's am bidh guilbnich " = "A corrie where curlew are found."
GROSSER BRACHVOGEL (*German*); LE COURLIS (*French*); WHAUP,
QUHAUP, OR FAUP (*Scottish*).

As the Tarmachan is essentially the true bird of the high
mountain lands, so the Curlew may be said to breathe
out the spirit of the lesser hills, of the rolling moors, remote, yet not entirely beyond human dwellings. There
are two bird notes I think inseparable with these moorlands. One is the vibrating, impassioned calling of the
Curlew; the other is the pipe of the Golden Plover. During the first days of March the moorlands are without
sound, seemingly without life even. And then the Curlews arrive in their hundreds. The country of heather
is silent no longer. On every side one hears, on these fine
mornings of early spring, whistling, trilling cries—cries
which are thrown far across the moors and re-echo through
the glens. But it is in a wood—one of those thickets of
naturally-sown Scots pines, the remnants of the great
Caledonian forest—that one realises what a strength
and power there are in the Curlew's love-song, for here
the notes resound, thrown back from many trees, in a
manner that compels attention.

Although the fact is not generally known, even amongst
bird lovers, few of the Curlew which make our hills such
happy places during the months of spring have wintered
in these Islands. True, there are representatives of the
species in their thousands to throng our mud flats during
short January days, but they have nested, not in Scot-

land, but in the High North, beyond, maybe, the Arctic
Circle. Our own Curlew, even before the approach of
winter—in early days of August, when the winds are still
warm on the hills, and when food, one imagines, must still
be plentiful—leave the moorlands and set their course
south. How far they travel is uncertain. Some winter
on Spanish coasts or on the shores of Portugal, but a
still more southerly point must be reached by many of
those Curlew which have laid their eggs and reared their
young on the hills of Scotland.

The air is soft and mild when the Curlew first arrive
at their upland nesting haunts, but as often as not, within
a space of a few days, even hours, of their arrival, winter
returns with its full severity. Blizzards sweep the moors,
pools and mosses become frozen fast, and the poor Whaups
have difficulty in obtaining a supply of food sufficient
to keep the spark of life alight. Many succumb to such
storms, many more fly feebly· to and fro, uttering hoarse,
husky cries quite unlike their usual clear, whistling notes.
Yet it never seems to enter their small minds that a flight
of, at the most, two hours' duration, would bring them
to the coast, where food must await them on the mud flats
of river estuaries even during the most severe weather.
Still, were they residents in the district—as is generally,
though erroneously, supposed—their line of conduct would
be more difficult to understand than if they knew these
Islands merely as their nesting site and quite unassociated
with hard weather.

For a week or so after their arrival on the hills the
Curlew keep together in flocks, but even before the opening days of April the majority have paired. It is during
April more than any month that the " white land " echoes
and re-echoes with the love-song of the Curlew. The singer,
flying along the moor a few yards above the surface of the
ground, checks his flight and rises almost perpendicularly,

with wings rapidly beating the air. On reaching a certain elevation he soars—glides rather—earthward, in a slanting direction, and it is now that his song is uttered. Commencing usually in a couple of long-drawn whistles, uttered in a very low key, the song quickens, the notes are sharper and clearer, and have at the middle of the " performance " a curious distinctive " break," difficult to put into words. It is at this point that the song is carried far across the moorland country—it can, it is stated, be heard three miles away, if everything be favourable—but almost at once the key is lowered, the calls become more subdued, more drawn out, until they end, as they commenced, in low, melancholy cries.

Sometimes one sees a Curlew making his way across a moor and constantly fluttering up into the air. But one imagines that there is something at fault, for time after time he utters only the first note of his song, and then almost at once mounts again into the heavens. Can it be that he does not succeed in reaching the correct altitude from which all self-respecting Curlew commence their appeals to their adored ones ? But perhaps the songster is not producing that bottom note satisfactorily, and thus is doing his best to perfect it. It is, I believe, only the male birds that practise these distinctive risings and dips in the air, but I can assert from personal experience the hen also makes use of the trilling, tuneful cries, which most ornithologists associate only with the cock bird during the season of nesting.

The Curlews are on the moorlands for close on two months before the first eggs are laid. During April of the present year (1914) quite remarkable weather conditions were experienced in the country of the hills. Day after day cloudless skies and mild breezes made it hard to realise that summer had not arrived, and so I was interested to see whether such exceptional temperatures would hasten the laying of the moorland birds. In the case of the Curlew, however, I am bound to say that the birds did not seem to be influenced in the least. I was nevertheless impressed by the remarkable punctuality in the laying of the birds in the district I had under observation, for on 27th April I saw three Curlews' nests the owner of each of which was at precisely the same stage in the production of her clutch. Even had the nests been near to each other this fact would have been worthy of setting down, but, as a matter of fact, a considerable distance separated them. Again, the elevations were different. One nest was about 500 feet above sea-level, the second 800 feet up, while the third was near the 1000 feet contour line. The nest of the Curlew is—as is the case with most "waders"—a primitive affair, being merely a hollow scraped out amongst the heather or rough grass and lined, perhaps, with a few grass stalks. It is sometimes placed on a "tussock" in a bog.

The eggs, four in number, are remarkably large for the size of the bird. They are pyriform in shape, and are usually, though not, be it noted, always, arranged with their small ends to the centre. In markings they are handsome. Some are of a buffish ground colour, others olive green, and in the same nest one may be found differing markedly from its fellows. The eggs are thickly spotted and blotched with dark grey-brown spots and blotches, and these are generally more numerous towards the larger end. The mother Curlew commences to sit after her second egg has been laid. These, it may be mentioned here, are *not* laid in the morning, and I believe that a day may elapse without an egg being deposited.

During the present season I spent some time in watching the behaviour of the Curlew of a certain rough meadow bordering on an upland river. A pair of birds about 100 yards from where an ornithologist companion and I

CURLEW'S NEST. THE EGGS ARE LYING IN AN UNUSUAL POSITION.

were concealed led us to believe, by their interesting
behaviour, that they had decided to nest near. The
hen—distinguished by her larger size and darker plumage
—was feeding not far from us when her mate appeared
on the scene. He seemed to be considerably annoyed
that she was not looking after her nest, for he pursued
her energetically backwards and forwards, endeavouring
to implant upon her person pecks from his long and sharp
bill. It was on the following day that we discovered the
nest. For quite a considerable time we watched a Curlew
feed among the wet grass land, and then, to our surprise,
she stopped suddenly and sat down so that only her head,
with its long curved bill, was visible. The nest was untidy,
and the eggs, two in number, had been partially hidden
by grass placed over them by the parent bird. We retreated once more, but it was some time before the bird
returned to her nest. She walked sedately amongst the
long grass, and once surprised and interested the writer
by uttering the vibrating song heard only during the
nesting, while she was standing on the ground ! A rock
lay on the moorland near the nest, and on to it she climbed,
falling sound asleep with her head half under her wing.
At times we could see one eye open, and she would lazily
stretch herself before dozing off once more. At length
she went back to her nest, and, as though to keep her
company, a Golden Plover arrived and mounted guard on
a knoll a few feet from her, before he flew off to look after
his own household affairs.

That same afternoon we made an expedition to the
high moorlands, and, as I mentioned above, found two
more Curlews' nests, each containing two eggs. Though
the full clutch had not been laid, the hen bird in each
instance was sitting fairly close, and when flushed circled
round us, uttering her shrill notes of alarm. One of the
nests was placed in very boggy ground—and, indeed, I

think that of all "waders" the Curlew at times chooses the most swampy localities in which to nest. Usually the wariest of birds, she occasionally shows a confidence which is quite surprising. On one occasion I came across a Curlew's nest where the owner did not appear to be so unapproachable as is generally the case, and so I determined to attempt to secure some photographs of her on the nest. It needed only two or three visits to implant a surprising amount of confidence into my "sitter," for at the end of this period I was able, by careful stalking, to approach to within a distance of six feet and to erect a half-plate camera without causing her to leave her eggs. And yet this bird, which was, to all appearances, a model mother, brought off three of her young, and then left the nest with them, abandoning her fourth egg, in which was a fully-developed chick—a chick which would have emerged from the shell if its mother had waited on only a few more hours.

A little earlier in this chapter I mentioned that the eggs of the Curlew were usually, though not invariably, placed in the nest with their small ends towards the centre. In such a position they take up less space, but a Curlew of my acquaintance evidently had her own ideas on the subject, and never, to my knowledge, had her eggs placed in the position favoured by every self-respecting member of the great family of "waders." A photograph of this particular nest is given as one of the illustrations of this chapter.

Although the Curlew is never met with far from the hills, still its nest is rarely placed at a greater elevation than 2000 feet above sea-level. It thus does not frequent the high hills where the Golden Plover has its home. A country entirely given over to heather is not looked on favourably by the Whaup, for here is an absence of its staple food—of worms and other dainties, which it probes for deep in the soft earth with its long, bent beak. The ideal ground is what is known in Northumberland as " white land "—great expanses of moorland grass, with many peat mosses scattered through it, and it is here that, more than anywhere, the moors re-echo with many reverberating whistling voices. Besides worms, the food of the Curlew at its summer quarters is varied. Insects and their larval forms are eaten, and the berries of the blaeberry (*Vaccinium myrtillus*) and the crowberry (*Empetrum nigrum*) are also consumed on occasion. Although inhabiting only the middle zone, as it were, of the hills, the Curlew never, so far as my experience goes, nests on the moors actually on the coast-line, though they are found quite a short distance—half a dozen miles or so— inland. Like other waders a number of " trial " nesting hollows are scraped out near the nest finally utilised, and it is said that these hollows may be the work of the cock bird, but so far as I know this point has never been investigated in the case of the Curlew, though with the Green Plover there is little doubt but that the cock amuses himself, and fills his wife with admiration, by pivoting himself round from one side to another during his display, forming the "scrapes" which are so much in evidence at the nesting site.

It is toward the end of May that the first of the baby Curlews emerge from the shell. They are able to run actively about almost from the moment of leaving the egg, and it is doubtless with a view to obtaining as vigorous chicks as possible that the Curlew, and indeed the majority of wading birds, lay such large eggs. Indeed I incline to the belief that, of all the waders, the chicks of the Curlew are the most vigorous when hatched.

On one occasion a Curlew had her nest in a moss at the foot of the Cairngorm mountains. Usually, on leaving the nest she flew off in comparative silence, but on the morning when I last visited the nesting site both she and the cock bird flew around in extreme anxiety, repeatedly uttering their usual cry, and also a curious distinctive chuckling note, which they make use of only when their young have been hatched out.

I remarked to the stalker who accompanied me that the birds must have hatched off their brood, but he informed me that he did not think this could be the case, for only the previous evening he had visited the nest and the eggs had then just commenced to chip. But a few hours had brought great changes with them, and not only were two of the young hatched off, but they were well grown and able to run actively about—indeed, it was only by means of considerable persuasion that they could be induced to remain in the nest while their photograph was being taken. On the upper mandible of the bill of each chick was plainly visible the hard encrusted growth by the help of which the young birds hammer through the shell, and thus emerge from their prison.

From time to time the parent birds crossed overhead, whistling and calling in alarm, and the chicks answered them with cries which strikingly resembled those of their elders, albeit they were yet somewhat husky through lack of practice.

In colour the Curlew chicks have the under surface of a yellowish grey, the upper parts being of the same colour, but with patches of dark brown distributed over them. Until the time when they are able to fly—about seven weeks—they are cared for most attentively by both parent birds. When she had eggs only to guard the Curlew often left the nest in silence, stealthily, nor did she put in an appearance while her treasures were being admired and examined. Her call note, if she indeed cried out at all, was the " courlie," which one ever associates with the Curlew at all seasons of the year. But when her small children are ushered into the world all this is changed.

At the first sighting of danger the mother bird—perhaps both parents together—rise excitedly, restlessly, from the moor, and fly round the object of their alarm, uttering the while anxious cries, resembling somewhat the words "whew-e-whro," and quite unlike their ordinary call or alarm notes. Sometimes, indeed, one of the birds will swoop down at your head, giving utterance to a wild shriek of distress. As the chicks crouch low on the ground at the first warning cry of their parents they are extremely hard to discover. One may search unsuccessfully for hours, and it really is more satisfactory to lie quietly and watch from some point of vantage until the young show themselves again under the impression that the danger has passed. The Curlew chicks are conducted by their parents on quite long excursions, and may not infrequently be seen in green grass fields, where their discovery is a much easier matter than out in the rough moorland.

Not after their young are strong on the wing do the Curlew remain on the hills. As early as the third week in June I have seen them migrating south, flying high before a northerly wind, and calling repeatedly as they passed, and by the Twelfth scarce a Curlew can be seen on the uplands anywhere. Even before that date our eastern coasts are already thronged with Curlew people from northerly lands, for although our own birds may, a few of them, winter on our coasts, the majority make their way south till the shores of Spain and Portugal are reached.

Doubtless because of its grotesquely long bill and its wild, sometimes almost unearthly cry, the Curlew has from earliest times been looked at askance. To the Highlanders the "Whaup" is often considered as being in league with the Evil One—in fact "Auld Whaup-neb" is a name for the devil—and its wail may portend disaster to the crofter who hears it.

It is often thus. The sound which to one ear may seem grand, striking, in its primitive, plaintive strength, to another may possess all those qualities which inspire dread, the dread of those who possess not understanding for the call of the wild. The name by which the Curlew is known to the Gaels is "Guilbinn." One will find, on consulting a Gaelic dictionary, that "Guilbinnach" is set down, but I believe that this latter word is a term applied rather to the Whimbrel than to the Great Curlew.

In the west they have—or perhaps it is only a few of a former generation—a charming name for the Curlew. To the old shepherd herding his flock above the deep sea lochs bordering the Atlantic the bird is *An t-Eun Chais-meachd* (the Bird of Alarm). A true name indeed, for the Curlew is the sentinel of the hills.

Though the Curlew could not but be considered as a peaceable bird, on a certain occasion, when making my way up a glen, I disturbed a Heron from his fishing at the burn side. A pair of Curlew had young near, and as the large bird passed their ground first one and then the other of the parents dashed out and with angry cries pursued the intruder fiercely. The Heron dodged and dived with no little concern till he had placed himself beyond the danger zone. Then one of the Curlews, desisting from the attack, soared off, and before alighting on a ridge threw out over the glen its vibrating whistling song, evidently thoroughly satisfied with its sally.

A quality which doubtless inspires respect and awe among the superstitious is the habit of the "lang nebbet whaap" which keeps it abroad throughout the hours of darkness. Recognised hours of sleep are unknown to it—it snatches rest at odd intervals throughout the whole twenty-four hours of the day. From the closing days of July till the end of March, or even later, our eastern coast-line—and to a lesser extent the western—harbours countless thousands of the Curlew tribe. When they first arrive they are confiding, with a confidence born of an ignorance of the habits of man, but inroads amongst their ranks are soon made by the shore gunner, and the Whaups become restless and difficult to approach. They obtain their food during this season mainly on the mud flats of river estuaries, but when compelled by the rising tide to beat a retreat they move in flocks a short distance inland, where they feed lazily till it is possible for them to return once more to the shore. They have been observed several miles from the tide to cease feeding in the fields, collect together, and wing their way to the sea at the very moment when the shallows were first exposed.

An explanation advanced to account for this interesting behaviour is that Curlew scouts are stationed within sight of the sea to give notice when first the feeding grounds are left bare. I would rather incline to the belief that the birds' sense of the progress of time is sufficiently accurate for them to feel instinctively when it is possible for them to return to their interrupted meal. During these months of winter the call note is usually a single one—" curlieu "— but at times, and especially if the weather is open and at all suggestive of spring, the birds utter the opening bars of the vibrating song characteristic of the nesting season. At such times the song is never, so far as my experience goes, finished—it is abruptly cut short, as though the singer suddenly realised that his vocal effort was premature, and, indeed, somewhat out of place. The Curlew is quite good eating, especially if it has left the moorlands only recently, but after a prolonged sojourn by the sea its marine diet renders it less sought after. There is an old saying to the effect that,

> " A Curlew lean, or a Curlew fat,
> Carries twelve pence on its back."

It is not everywhere, however, that the Curlew is eaten.

THE GREENSHANK

TRINGA NEBULARIA

DEOCH-BHUIDH (*Gaelic*); CHEVALIER GRIS (*French*); HELLFARBIGER WASSERLAÜFER (*German*); OOLITBOLSCHOI (*Russian*).

SHOULD ever a poetical name be sought after for the Greenshank, one that would suit it well is The Bird with the Restless Spirit. I think that even the Curlew himself must yield second place to him in watchfulness.

The Greenshank is met with over the majority of Great Britain as a passing migrant only, and there are very few nesting haunts of the species south of Inverness. A well-known nesting site of the birds, where I have recently been studying them, is sadly overrun by collectors who let no opportunity pass of making themselves possessors of so great a prize as a clutch of Greenshank's eggs, and I fear that the birds are decreasing at this, their farthest south stronghold.

During the second week in May, 1914, the head stalker of the forest and I spent a good deal of time in hunting over suitable Greenshank ground, but saw no signs of a nest. The stalker knew the habits of the Greenshank well, and he told me that he had invariably before found nests even when he was not searching for them. I had my only sight of the birds during the second day's search. In passing a lochan a pair of Greenshank rose from where they had probably been feeding and made their way quickly over the moor in silence. I had previously heard, while searching for the nest, what I imagined was the cry of one of the birds overhead, but did not succeed in catching a glimpse of him. The nesting-ground was not far

THE HAUNT OF THE GREENSHANK.

removed from the nesting site of the Crested Tit, but was farther out into the moor.

Several years previously a big heather fire had got out of hand, and had burnt a large tract of ground, including a number of pine trees. Previous to this Greenshank were not numerous in the locality, but the bare and blackened moor was evidently to their liking, for a number put in their appearance the following year, and frequented the spot regularly until the present season. The birds arrived early in April, usually paired, and the full clutch of eggs could usually be found on May 12th. On one occasion a great storm of snow descended on the nesting ground of the Greenshank after some of the birds had commenced to brood. One of the stalkers on the forest had discovered a nest a day or two previously, and visited the spot during the storm, when no less than 14 inches of snow covered the ground. So deep was the snow that he was unable to locate the exact place where the nest was situated, but in his search he happened to tread on a branch concealed out of sight by the white covering on the ground. At once the sitting Greenshank broke through the snow, where she had been brooding on her eggs, quite buried from view, and fluttered out with difficulty. This incident speaks well for the hardiness of a bird which is only a summer migrant to these Islands.

In many ways the Greenshank is eccentric in its habits, and one of its peculiarities is that it must have some definite landmark against which to deposit its eggs. Its nesting grounds are moorlands with a few scattered pines growing through them, and there are usually scattered about dead pine branches, or the stumps of former trees still hold themselves a foot or so above the surface of the ground. The nest is invariably to be found placed beside one of these landmarks ; it is never in a tussock or on a knoll, as is the case with the Redshank, and thus, to one

N

who knows this idiosyncrasy, the nest is not so difficult
to discover as would be the case otherwise. Should tree
stumps or fallen branches be absent, the Greenshank
makes its nest against a stone, but this is the exception
in the nesting grounds which I know.

Like some other " waders," the Greenshank is in the
habit of making several false nests or " scrapes " in the
vicinity of the true nest, and it may be that these are
formed by the male bird in the course of his display. The
nest is a slight depression neatly made and of no great
depth. At times it is lined with pieces of bark pulled by
the Greenshank from the branch against which the nest
is placed, or a few blades of grass or pieces of lichen are
utilised.

The eggs are usually four in number, but I am informed
by a stalker that he once found a clutch of five. They
are handsome and quite characteristic. The ground
colour is usually of a pale buff, and the eggs are thickly
marked with a distinctive shade of dark brown. The
underlying shell-marks are more apparent than is the case
with the eggs of any " wader " I know. The behaviour
of the bird during the time she is brooding varies greatly.
At times it is possible to approach to within a few feet
of the nest without causing her to leave, or she may be so
wary as to rise from her eggs before it is possible to mark
her departure. The Greenshank, as I mentioned earlier,
usually chooses as a nesting site a piece of moor recently
burnt—she never rests amongst full-grown heather—and
so it is not easy to approach her unobserved.

Though so wary and suspicious a bird, she sometimes
nests in the vicinity of houses. The stalker of a certain
Inverness-shire forest showed me in 1914 a Greenshank's
nest within five minutes' walk of his home. On May 21st
the last egg was laid, and the bird commenced to brood,
but owing, perhaps, to the fact that a pair of Curlew had

their nest near, and gave the alarm in no uncertain manner when danger approached, the Greenshank always sat lightly; in fact, it was only on one occasion that I saw her leave the nest at all. During her flight, too, she remained silent, and it was after we had been at the nest some time that she put in an appearance, flying restlessly round once till she lighted on the very top of a Scots pine, and uttered her wild and striking whistle before winging her way right out of sight. Presuming that the hen did the main share of incubation—she was at no time sufficiently near to be identified—the cock never put in an appearance. The nest in this case was placed at the foot of a decaying tree stump, and there was a complete absence of cover for the brooding bird. For many miles around there extended great pine forests; indeed, the woods approached to within less than 100 yards of the nest. In the background the whole range of the Cairngorm Hills lay clear in the strong June sunlight. On Cairngorm itself broad fields of snow still lingered. Coire an t-sneachdach still held great fields of white, though I have often wondered why this title of Snowy Corrie has not been given to Coire Lochan, farther to the west of the hill, for here the snowbeds linger as often as not throughout the year.

In Coire Caise the burn draining the corrie still flowed deep beneath its snowy covering, but from Creag na Leachann the hand of winter had departed for a season. From the haunt of the Greenshank one looked right through the Larig Ghruamach, that deep pass, full of gloom and grandeur, which stretches through the very heart of the great hill range. The pass is high—at its summit the sea lies near 3000 feet below it—and its dark sides were still flecked with snow. In the far distance, too, one could see the birth-place of the Dee, and where the river, emerging from its tunnel of snow, dropped in white cascades into the glen below.

Amid such surroundings of grandeur and solitude
the Greenshank had her home. And not far from her
nest, on the far side of a narrow belt of pines, a second
pair of birds had made their haunt in the earlier part of
the season.   Their scrapes I found—in the shelter of the
inevitable fir branches—and also what I think was the true
nest, placed against a small tree stump ; but of the eggs,
or of the birds themselves, there were no signs. I am
doubtful, even, whether the bird whose nest forms the
illustration to this chapter hatched off her brood.

On June 12th I visited her nesting site for the purpose
of photographing the young Greenshanks. As I passed
through the trees bordering the moss I heard curious
chortling cries which I am at a loss to describe, or to liken
to any other note in the bird world, proceeding from a
tree a few yards distant. On the very summit of this
tree was perched my friend the Greenshank, but almost
at once she took her departure, uttering her characteristic
wild whistle.   I crossed over to the nest and found the eggs
had gone, but there were no signs of small pieces of egg-
shell lying in the nest—and these should have been present
if the young had been safely hatched. I returned to the
moss later in the day, coming across from the opposite
quarter, but failed to see or hear the parent bird again,
although I searched a good extent of the nesting area.
It would almost seem as though the eggs had been taken,
for the Greenshank when she has young is usually the
most anxious of parents, fluttering above the head of the
person crossing her ground and uttering wild cries of alarm.
Her anxiety for her young continues even after these
have reached the age at which they are strong on the
wing, as the following incident will show. One early
morning of mid-July I was approaching a certain hill loch
which lay far below me, with waters unruffled by even
the faintest breeze. Through the glass I was watching

a Goosander in her fishing operations when I heard, coming from the moss at the end of the loch, yelping cries which at this far distance sounded for all the world like the call notes of the Peregrine Falcon. But a nearer approach showed me that a Greenshank was uttering her call of alarm, and, as I considered that she must have young somewhere near, I lay on the edge of the moss and kept under observation the area from which the parent bird had risen.

After a time there emerged from the lcng, mossy grass a young Greenshank, which bobbed and curtsied in characteristic manner as it surveyed the scene, which it imagined to be clear of danger. From the anxiety of the parent bird, I imagined that the youngster could not yet be capable of looking after itself, but as I walked up to where it was standing, it took wing without hesitation. Its mother at once joined it, and together they disappeared from sight, the adult bird still uttering her cry of alarm.

Another nesting site of this interesting bird which I visited in June of 1914 was on the fringe of the Greenshank country.

It was late in the evening as the stalker and I approached the nesting ground. For the first time in his experience, the whole of the forest had failed to produce a single Greenshank's nest ; not even a scrape had we been able to discover, and so it was satisfactory to hear the alarm note of the bird as she moved elusively above the pine trees to our right. After a search we came across several scrapes, and then, situated against a fallen branch on a strip of heather burnt during the spring, the nest itself. The eggs had hatched safely off, to all appearances, for the nest contained small fragments of chipped shell, but the young must have left some days previously, and we did not see any traces of them. It is worthy of mention that one rarely, if ever, sees a pair of Greenshank at the nesting site, or guarding the young. The male birds of the species are said to roam far from their mates during the nesting season, and do not, as the Redshank, take their share in the rearing of the brood. The Redshank too does not appear to frequent the same country as does his relative of the green legs, for I did not see a single one at any of the nesting sites of the Greenshank that I visited.

The peculiarity of the Greenshank in perching on trees is well marked ; one of these birds will rarely alight on the ground if a Scots pine is in the neighbourhood, and it may well be owing to this habit that nesting sites with a few pines scattered through them are chosen in preference to treeless areas ; for it is in such pine-scattered situations that the Greenshank nests not only in Scotland, but through the whole of Northern Europe.

It is curious that a northern nesting bird like the Greenshank should find the winter in Great Britain too inclement for it, yet such is the case. During August and September numbers of the birds are seen on migration throughout the country south of the Tweed, but I believe that the south of Ireland is the only district where they remain throughout the winter.

The first authenticated instance of the Greenshank nesting in Scotland occurred about 1835, when MacGillivray found the eggs in Harris. Since then it has been found in the Moray basin, and in several of the most north-lying Scottish counties. Its nest has been discovered in Skye and in the Hebrides, and also, it is said, in the Shetlands.

During its stay on the moorlands the food of the Greenshank consists of worms, of beetles and insects, with their larval forms, but in winter on the coast it may feed on small fry of various kinds and on crabs and shrimps.

If hard pressed, both old and young Greenshanks

are able to take to the water, though they do not do so under ordinary conditions. One has been known, however, to throw itself repeatedly under water in order to escape the attentions of a Hawk. During the nesting season the Greenshank is essentially an Arctic bird. It is found in the wild districts of Scandinavia, and is numerous in Finland and in Northern Russia. In Asia it extends north to beyond 65 degrees, and eastward is found in Kamschatka. It winters in the basin of the Mediterranean, and through Africa it extends as far south as Cape Colony. Those Greenshank with their nesting quarters in Northern Asia go south, with the approach of the cold weather, to the Indian Ocean and east to China and Japan. During the cold season it also visits the Malay Archipelago, Tasmania, and Australia.

Description.—Head and neck light grey, heavily lined with lighter grey. Amongst the interscapulars are many black feathers margined with white. Long inner secondaries ash grey, spotted on margins with darker grey. Lower back and rump pure white; upper tail coverts white, barred with black. Tail white with black bars. Wing coverts dusky brown; major coverts barred with black. Primaries black, the outermost having white shafts. Under parts white. Side of head, neck and forebreast white, lined with black. Flanks barred with black. Bill black. Legs and feet green. Iris dark brown. After the autumn moult the upper parts are greyer and are less heavily striated. The full-fledged young are dark brown above with buff margins to the feathers. The downy young are pale buff above, with a triangular black spot on the crown, and the black loral stripe continued backwards behind the eye to merge with the black line on the nape. Back marked by median and lateral stripes of black. Under parts white.

THE GOLDEN PLOVER

CHARADRIUS PLUVIALIS

FEADAG (WHISTLER), FEADAG-BHUIDHE (*Gaelic*); PLUVIER DORÉ (*French*); GOLDENER REGENPFEIFER (*German*). Local names : — YELLOW PLOVER, GREY PLOVER, WHISTLING PLOVER, SHEEP'S GUIDE.

"The deep-toned Plover Grey, wild whistling on the hill."

IT is but natural that a bird with so plaintive and melancholy a cry as the Golden Plover should have more than one legend woven around it by the imaginative people of the western seaboard. By them the Feadag is known to feed on the wind, on the wild wind that sweeps in from the broad Atlantic, because of its great offence committed close on two thousand years ago. For it is known to the Gael that in the first of the Plover tribe there dwelt the souls of those Jews who assisted at the crucifixion of Christ. So through the ages the Plovers have no peace ; they call wildly, mournfully, for very shame at the great sin of their forbears, and they frequent the desolate and remote places where they may seek out from Nature the healing that she alone can give them.

The Golden Plover is more a lover of the solitary places than the Curlew. It arrives on the hills often before February is out, and right up to December large flocks may be seen frequenting the high moorlands. But it is more than probable that these Plover, seen so late in the season, are wanderers from the High North resting awhile on their southern migration. In like manner there appear in late spring, when our own birds are already busy with family cares, flocks of Golden Plover which are on their way to Northern Norway and Lapland, where

the land is still deep under snow, in spite of the light from
the midnight sun. I have seen such a company of Plover
as late as the third week in May, and at the time was at a
loss to account for their appearance.

While the Curlew is rarely found nesting above the
2000-foot level, the Golden Plover is found on the great
mosses of the Highlands quite 1000 feet higher, and I have
occasionally seen them at a height of 4300 feet above the
sea. On one occasion, while on the plateau of Braeriach,
itself at the 4000-feet level, I had an excellent view of a
Golden Plover as he flew across from out of the west.
Long before he was visible his clear-toned whistle was
borne down the wind, and the bird crossed over the
plateau at great speed, the snow-covered ground and the
Dee running beneath its white blanket—though the season
was early September—having little attraction for the
Feadag. On the Moine Mhor—the great moss stretching
away for miles on the borders of Aberdeenshire and
Inverness-shire, on which many burns have their birth-
place, the voice of the Golden Plover is the only sound to
break the stillness of this country of mist and storms.
April is giving place to May ere the Plover reach the Great
Moss, for its surface carries the winter snows long, and the
springs are frost-bound, yielding up no food for the Plover
tribe. But on the lower-lying moors and " white land "
the courting of the Plover takes place during March and
April, and by the third week of the latter month some of
the more forward of the birds are already brooding.

During the season of courtship, and indeed up to June,
is heard the song of the Golden Plover, and this song is
one of the most striking things in the habits of moorland
birds. Before commencing to sing, the cock bird mounts
into the air to a height of at least 100 feet, and flies slowly,
deliberately around the spot where his mate is listening
to him below, uttering as he flies a musical whistling cry

of two syllables sounding like " whee-wheeu," the last being long drawn out. His flight during this time is quite distinctive—he no longer cleaves the air with sharp and rapid wing-beats, but moves his wings with slow, deliberate strokes, holding them V-shaped for an instant between the beats. Should he cease his song—even for a few moments—the normal flight is at once resumed. His cry on these occasions carries over a great stretch of moor, and, I think, can be heard at a greater distance even than the vibrating notes of the Curlew. One day recently, while salmon-fishing on the river Dee, a Golden Plover for some time cruised overhead, singing loudly, but his notes had been audible for some time before I could locate the singer. Neither the picturesqueness of his flight nor the pleasant pitch of his voice appealed to the gillie, who asked, in a tone more than a little sarcastic, " What's he shoutin' up there for, anyway ? " After some time, during which these long-drawn whistles are regularly continued, the singer shoots earthward, uttering, just as he is reaching the ground, a curious purring cry, repeated rapidly five or six times. On paper the sounds resemble " Trōōeu, trōōeu, trōōeu."

It is only in a very few localities that the nesting site of the Feadag descends to the level of the big Scottish rivers. One moor there is which I have in mind where, bordering the Dee, and at a height of less than 400 feet above sea-level, at least two pairs of Golden Plover nest annually. Shut in from the winds of the north by rising ground, and fully exposed to the sun, this little moor is the earliest nesting site of the Golden Plover in the whole district, and here, as early as May 10th, I have seen a young brood close on a week old.

Although feeding largely on soft, boggy ground, the Rain Bird—as the Plover is sometimes termed—does not usually choose such wet sites for its nesting as does the Curlew. I have found the nest on more than one occasion close to a hill-top where no marshy land was visible, even at a distance, and the eggs, as far as my experience goes, invariably have a dry bed. Even before the exact nesting site has been chosen, the birds are nervous and restless when approached, uttering their whistle repeatedly until they rise from the moor and wing their way right out of sight.

After the eggs have been laid, the cock bird mounts guard on some raised ground within a hundred yards or so of the nest, and remains motionless for hours on sentinel duty. He is quick to spy out an intruder as he approaches, and at once calls sharply, repeating his call at intervals of a few seconds. On learning from her mate that danger is near, the hen Golden Plover rises unseen from the nest and runs quietly through the heather for some distance before she also adds her own alarm cry to that of the cock.

It is not always that her husband warns her, and at times such as these she will sit very close, being thus quite unlike the Lapwing, who is always on the alert for danger when brooding, and who takes wing when the intruder is yet some distance away. And how elusive, how deceptive, the call of the Whistler is ! At times one imagines that the bird is close at hand, and one looks in vain for the well-known form. But now comes again the cry of the bird, this time faint, indistinct, and one realises that the owner of the voice is in reality several hundred yards distant. When mist is low on the hills, it is often possible to approach birds which are nominally shy and wary. On a certain occasion I was walking over high ground enveloped in mist, and almost trod upon a Golden Plover covering her eggs. She remained there quietly until my back was turned, then slipped off into the cloud. Only a day or two later I revisited the nesting ground in fine weather, and, evidently sighting me from a distance, the Plover had left the nest long before I had reached it. During the spring of 1914 I spent some time studying the Golden Plover at its upland haunts. One nest I saw was situated on a wide open moor near to a circular sheep shelter (known to farmers as a stell).

Though May had not arrived, the hen bird was sitting very close, and when disturbed fluttered along the ground with trailing wings, practising the well-established deception so common in the bird world. All the time I was at the nest the Plover flew round anxiously, repeatedly calling in her plaintive whistle, and when I left the spot she was so near that it seemed she would quickly return to the nest. Although I waited for some time behind the shelter, the bird could not make up her mind to venture back on to her eggs.

For quite a long time she wandered round, from time to time picking up an insect which her sharp eye had located. Once, while walking quickly over some uneven ground, she stumbled on the edge of a tussock of grass, almost losing her balance, and appearing ludicrous in the extreme in her efforts to regain it. The cock bird was not to be seen ; he may have been away feeding, but certainly he did not come near to lend his moral support to his wife.

The eggs of the Golden Plover are always four in number. The nest and nesting sites often resemble those of the Green Plover, but the eggs are larger and more handsome. The ground colour varies. It may be of an olive green or of a buff-coloured brown, and on this ground colour large marks of rich red brown are laid over the eggs, the markings being generally more numerous towards the larger end. The nest is markedly deeper than that of the Lapwing. It is rarely placed in long heather, but short heather of about eight years of age is much utilised as a nesting site. The nest is scantily lined with pieces of lichen or dried stems of grass.

The young remain in the nest only a few hours after hatching off. They are prettily-coloured chicks, clad in down of pale golden yellow, and mottled over with black, their under parts are white. Over each eye runs a white lateral stripe, and this line continues down the back; when fledged they are brownish black, spotted with bright yellow above.

Even when the young are just hatching off, the parent bird at times broods very lightly, and leaves the nest when the intruder is still quite 100 yards distant. I have noticed that sometimes both Plover call repeatedly until one has actually discovered the nest, when they stand about quietly, realising that it is no longer possible to lead one away from their eggs or young.

On Morven, in Aberdeenshire, a great many pairs of Golden Plover nest every spring, and even above the 2000-feet contour they have quite a number of Lapwings as their companions. It is of interest here to note the difference in the behaviour of the two different species when their nesting ground is invaded. The Lapwing, ever on the alert, move backward and forward over their ground with tireless energy. But the Golden Plover rarely take wing, though they, too, are sensible that their home is being invaded; they stand quietly near, and their piping cry resounds through the moor. The flight, too, of the Golden Plover has little resemblance to that of the Lapwing. It is not so erratic as that of the Peewit, and the bird can forge through the air at great speed with little effort, whereas with the Lapwing rapid and sustained flight is unusual.

Again, the Golden Plover is a peace-loving bird, the Lapwing a born fighter. Any feathered visitor, from a Starling to a Heron, is driven off with fury by the Green

Plover should it be so unwary as to venture near the nesting grounds of the Feadag. But I have rarely seen a Golden Plover fly out to the attack.

Not infrequently a big snowfall sweeps over the higher hills during the early days of May, piling up great wreaths on the sheltered south slopes where the Plover nest, and forcing them to leave their eggs. At such times the unfortunate birds congregate once more into flocks and frequent the fields at the foot of the glens. If they have only just commenced to brood they will deposit fresh clutches of eggs after the storm and hope for kinder weather conditions.

It is on account of its gift in foretelling the approach of stormy weather that the Golden Plover has been termed the Rain Bird. Before rain or wind the birds retire inland, should they be at their winter quarters on the coast, and they are never known to be misled in their forecast.

The food of the Golden Plover varies with its quarters. When on the moors it often collects in numbers, on some crofter's small field lying in the heart of the hills, to feed on the worms and beetles found amongst the young grass. It is also partial to larvæ and to the seeds of certain plants. The young, too, live chiefly on insects. In winter, when on the coast, the Plovers feed mainly on marine animals, molluscs and the like, but not being equipped with a bill like that of the Curlew, they are at a considerable disadvantage as compared to the latter bird in their food-hunting on the mud-flats. For this reason, perhaps, the Plover is not such a marine feeder as the Curlew, for it frequents the fields bordering on the sea even more than the coast-line itself. During autumn and winter the Golden Plover is much sought after by the shore gunners, for it makes excellent eating. After a time of persecution the birds become wary and difficult to approach, but before they have learnt their lesson, if one out of a flock is shot and falls to the ground its companions wheel about and return to the spot, calling loudly in an attempt to induce their dead comrade to rejoin them.

Compared with the Lapwing, the Feadag is a late nesting bird, and for several reasons his nesting may become unusually protracted. Breeding as he does on the very exposed moorlands, he is greatly dependent on the weather for the successful hatching of the eggs. Many enemies surround him and his mate in their wild haunts. Grey Crows move silently past, on the keen look-out for booty of any kind, and foxes have their home on the high tops.

Even in mid-July the Feadag may still be busy with family cares. I shall for long hold pleasant memories of a day that I spent on a certain wild hill during the early part of July, a hill where many a Golden Plover was still tending her young.

It was early morning when we left our base. The sun already shone warmly, and the glen was full of life, but away westward the big hill was in gloom, and at times grey clouds just touched its summit. For some distance the way led up a wide strath through which there flowed a burn now running dead low as the result of successive weeks of drought. Its pools held many a trout, some of which must have turned the scales at considerably over a pound. From the bushes of broom, and from the bracken on the hillside, Whinchats called incessantly with their metallic alarm cry. They had families, all of them, and strongly resented the intrusion into their nesting sites. Pairs of Sandpipers were tending their chicks at the burn side, and a Dipper, rising at our feet, flew off uttering his sharp alarm note.

The ground hereabouts is given over to sheep ; Grouse there are, it is true, but they are regarded as a secondary consideration. Thus it was that we were not surprised to see a family of no less than seven Carrion Crows, of evil and forbidding mien, rise from the hill before us and fly unsuspiciously away. Such a sight would have stirred the most stoical Grouse-preserver, for no Carrion or Hooded Crow is tolerated where the Red Bird is shot. For three miles our way led us up the strath, then, striking off to the right, we commenced our climb. The sun shone with great heat as we gradually left the glen below us. Before us lay a great corrie, with dark crags leading down into a small burn far beneath them. Here the Peregrine has his eyrie, and during the season when we visited the glen, a pair of the Falcons had nested close to the ledge of rock where a Raven had successfully brought off her young earlier in the season. The young Corbies had, in all probability, already left the nest before the Falcon scraped her primitive hollow and deposited her handsome eggs, otherwise it must have been a circumstance well worthy of record that Falcon and Raven should thus have nested side by side in harmony. On the lower slopes of the hill bird life was almost non-existent, save for a Meadow Pipit which fluttered off its nest before us, and literally tumbled down the hill in its efforts to distract our attention.

It was not till we had reached an elevation of close on 2500 feet that we heard the first pipe of a watchful Feadag. And now from all sides we heard such cries, borne across on the breeze from the higher grounds. One Golden Plover by his behaviour led me to suspect that even at this late season his mate was still brooding on eggs, for as we passed he merely called a few times without changing his position, then lapsed into silence. If his brood had been in the neighbourhood, I think he must have showed more anxiety. Not once, but several times, we heard a Golden Plover uttering his characteristic love-song, and noted the singer as he moved rapidly over the hill plateau. Here we stood at an elevation of close on

3000 feet, where even under the most favourable conditions May must be well advanced before the Plover migrants commence to lay. But they are lucky if they hatch off their first brood—if they escape the glance of the Raven and the Carrion Crow, and if the hill fox spares them. So it is that second nests are by no means uncommon on the hill.

On the hill-top the ground stretches away for miles in a great plateau, with many peat hags and a few lochans catching the sun as they lie there. Masses of cloudberry carpet the ground, and the club moss (*Lycopodium selago*) grows more profusely than I have ever seen it elsewhere.

One Golden Plover we came across had young of a tender age, and displayed more anxiety on their behalf than I have ever known of the Feadag tribe. At first she ran around uttering her plaintive pipe, and on my essaying an imitation of the cry of a chick in distress she crouched flat on the ground, endeavouring to persuade me that she was brooding her young, and practising a deception which I became so familiar with while studying the Dotterel at her nesting site. Presently, tiring of this ruse, she ran down the hill with tail outspread, and waving one wing in the air. She certainly feigned a broken wing with exceptional skill, the way in which she held it high and waved it feebly being masterly to a degree.

Later on, finding that I remained unresponsive despite her finished acting, the Plover ran back towards me. At times she paused, then gradually fluffed on the feathers before giving them a quick shake, in true Dotterel fashion. Like the Dotterel, too, she fed on any insect her sharp eye detected, despite her anxiety. When I rose up and started out for another part of the hill, the Feadag evidently imagined that my move was the result of her manœuvring, and showed great gratification, flying and running on

o

ahead of me until she imagined she had decoyed me far enough from her brood, when she wheeled back and joined her family.

The sun was low when we left the hill-top. A Grouse fluttered away at our feet, disclosing a family of ten young chicks, which crouched flat on the ground until they began to feel the cold wind. Then they rose together and, cheeping shrilly, ran off in all directions, their progress being so precipitate that they constantly were thrown head over heels, but were off again none the worse the next moment. From patches of " scree " Wheatears chacked their displeasure before taking flight. But the most beautiful sight of the day was, when looking over into the corrie, we saw one of the Peregrines sailing across the face of the rock. The sun glinted full on its plumage, and it was clearly marked against the black rocks, already deep in the shadow of the evening. Backwards and forwards across the rock face the Peregrine circled, dipping and gliding with the poetry of unrivalled flight. Several times it made as though to alight, but for some time yet we saw it till it came to rest on what was probably its roosting ledge. Through the glass I could make out a hollow in the cliff which, from the characteristic white droppings on the rock below, seemed as though it must be the Falcon's eyrie, unless, indeed, the Raven had led forth her young from this point when the spring had yet scarcely reached the hills.

Not a single Curlew did we hear during this long day on the hill : one missed their vibrating cries in a country which should certainly have harboured a few representatives. The air was still as we reached the strath below, and the murmur of the burn carried far to-night. In the glen the sun had already set, but on the hill, now clear of even a trace of cloud, it yet shone with a warm, red glow, while to the nor'-west the sky was of that deep and wonder-

ful red which presages the coming of fine weather to the
country of the hills.

By far the majority of Golden Plover seen on the
coasts of Britain during the winter months are northern
migrants, and, as I mentioned earlier in this chapter, flocks
returning to the High North pass over us up to the opening
days of June. During autumn evenings big companies
of Golden Plover and Curlew pass high above the midland
counties of England on their way from their nesting
grounds. The birds usually fly in the form of a wedge
and at a great height, their whistling cries sounding faint
and far off. On quiet winter days, when thick banks of
fog hold the coast-line, the Golden Plover at times lose
their bearings in the white mists. I have seen them
emerge suddenly out of the gloom, calling to each other
repeatedly as they flew. For a time they are swallowed
up in the fog. Then they reappear, flying aimlessly in
circles, for they are strangers and in a strange land where
many unknown dangers may await them.

As a nesting species in England the Golden Plover is of
local occurrence, but on the Border country is numerous.
As far south as Devon and Cornwall it breeds sparingly,
and is found also on the North Staffordshire moors. In
Scotland and Ireland it is found in numbers on suitable
ground. It nests in the Hebrides, Orkney, and Shetland.
Northwards it breeds on the Faroe Islands, and in Scandinavia is numerous. It is on the tundras of Northern
Russia that the Golden Plover has its headquarters, where
it rears its young far from all human habitations.

A well-known ornithological authority has written
that the Golden Plover and Ptarmigan of the far north,
or those nesting at high elevations, assume a more handsome dress at the approach of the nesting season than
do their confrères farther south or on lower ground. In
this country I have not investigated the question as

regards the Golden Plover, but recent expeditions over Ptarmigan ground have shown me that the Ptarmigan nesting on the high plateaux over 3000 feet above sea-level showed noticeably richer and more striking tints of plumage than a bird examined on a grouse moor 500 feet or more below the former altitude.

Winter comes early to the lands within the Arctic Circle, and thus it is that even while summer still lingers with us, the advance guard of the northern hosts of waders begin to appear on our moorlands and shores. These early arrivals are chiefly young birds which make the southern stage immediately they are sufficiently strong on the wing to do so. Right up to November fresh arrivals pass over us, or perhaps take up their winter quarters on our coasts. Vast flocks of Golden Plover cross Heligoland every autumn on their way to their southern winter quarters, coming from the fjords and tundras of the north. Some of these voyagers traverse the North Sea and winter on our coasts, others pass south along the coast-lines to Spain, and from there press on to Northern Africa. Their principal winter quarters are said to be in the basin of the Mediterranean. The birds nesting in Siberia pursue a different southerly course, passing over Russia into the Crimea and thence as far south as Palestine.

Description.—So striking are the changes of plumage in the Golden Plover that Linnæus imagined two distinct species to exist. In summer he gave it the name *Charadrius apicarius*, while in winter it was to him *Charadrius pluvialis.*

In the plumage of the pairing season the male has the upper parts black, mixed sparingly with golden yellow. On the hinder scapulars a yellow band is present. The wing coverts are dark grey tipped with yellow, except those on the margins, which are white-tipped. The tail is dark, and is partially barred with creamy white. The under parts are mostly black, with the exception of the tail coverts, which are white. The bill and the legs are black. The female closely resembles the male in her plumage. After the autumn moult, which is commenced in September and is usually completed by November, the sides of the face and breast are white, the foreneck coloured with yellow, on which show dusky mottlings. The major coverts are tipped with white. The male is slightly the bigger bird—he is about $10\frac{3}{4}$ inches in length, and the extent of his wings are $22\frac{1}{4}$ inches. The female is $10\frac{1}{2}$ inches long, and her wings are 22 inches from tip to tip.

THE DOTTEREL

CHARADRIUS MORINELLUS

PLUVIER GUIGNARD (*French*); ZUEKGLUPÖI (*Russian*);
DÜTCHEN (*German, local*).

LONG summer days spent on the high tops in the mist-
country pass before the mind as I sit down to endeavour
to give some account of a bird which, by its trustfulness
and engaging habits, gives many a cheerful hour to the
ornithologist who studies it at its nesting sites on the
Roof of Scotland.

In earlier times the delightfully confiding character
of the Dotterel met with but scant appreciation, and the
bird was set down as a brainless individual deserving of
little but ridicule. The very name, Dotterel, is a deriva-
tive from the verb to " dote," while its scientific cognomen
is said to have its origin in *morus*—a fool. Then to the hill-
man the bird is known as *An t-amadan mointeach*, a term
signifying the " stupid fellow of the peat-mosses."

This confidence of the Dotterel has had a regrettable
effect on the numbers of the bird in this country. In
former times it was, I believe, found nesting on, the
Mendip Hills, and was also commonly seen on the Chilton
ridges in Berkshire and the chalk hills of Bedford, Hert-
ford, and Cambridge. Sir John Crewe wrote in 1865 that
he had often heard from his gamekeepers that it was quite
easy, fifteen or twenty years before that date, to shoot
Dotterel when they had young on the hills lying on the
borders of Derby and Stafford. Even at the present time
the birds make a halt at their old haunts during their

migration to less frequented localities, though no nest has been discovered for a good many years now. Until comparatively recent times a number nested every year on the high tops of the Lake District, notably on Skiddaw, but they have now ceased to visit this part of the country except on the migration northward, although an occasional pair may at times rear their young in the wildest and most inaccessible portions of the Pennine Range.

The Dotterel now has a restricted area as a nesting species in these Islands, and is, in fact, confined to the wildest parts of the Grampians, where it produces a family at an elevation of three or four thousand feet above the sea. It has always appeared to me to be a point of considerable interest that "the moss-fool" should be unable to remain in this country throughout the winter, while its near relative, the Golden Plover, spends the dark and short days on the mud flats round our coast-line.

The contrast in the winter habits of the two birds is the more surprising when it is realised that the nesting sites of the Dotterel are on the most exposed hill-tops and plateaux, where they have during this season of cares and responsibilities only the Ptarmigan as a companion, with perhaps an Eagle or two on his hunting foray; while the Golden Plover choose nesting grounds which are, at times, but a few hundred feet above sea-level, and only in exceptional conditions are they found breeding at levels where the Dotterel have their home from May to August. It cannot, I think, be that conditions of food-supply are the cause of this southern migration, for the food of the Dotterel and Golden Plover is much the same; but it may be that the Dotterel, being of slimmer build, is also thinner skinned, and as a result is less able to bear cold weather.

That the Dotterel does find these Islands an unsuitable home during the winter months is amply borne out

by the fact that only a single representative of the species
has been secured in this country during the winter—it
was shot on Dartmoor on December 12th, 1886.

The Dotterel arrive in this country towards the end of
April or commencement of May, and are said to make the
long migration flight from North Africa in the course
of a single night, since no records are to hand of their
having been observed at any intermediate halting-place
at this season. For some weeks after their arrival the
birds frequent the low grounds, feeding on various insects
in the fields, and it is not until near the end of May that
they leave civilisation and make their way to the highest
and most remote hill-tops, where they will rear their small
families amidst Alpine surroundings.

It is quite an interesting point that this diminutive
Plover almost invariably chooses as a nesting site the hill
summits or plateaux, and on the hill slopes is very uncommonly met with during the nesting season. I am
inclined to think that this can be explained by the fact
that *An t-amadan mointeach* is a great walker, running
quickly and easily over the short moss and crowberry
plants before the intruder, and hesitating to take flight
unless actually forced to do so. Now the vegetation on
the hillside is more dense and luxuriant than on the tops,
for the common heather (*Calluna vulgaris*) holds its stems
erect to a distance of a foot or more above ground, and
as a result the energetic and lively Dotterel is greatly
restricted in its movements.

At the present time the Dotterel is, I regret to say, a
diminishing species in Scotland—its last stronghold in
these Islands—but will continue to hold its own, against
its enemies at all events, in several of its exposed nesting grounds. Since Dotterel eggs are in great demand
with collectors at the present day, and since the birds
themselves are in requisition to yield up their plumage

to the salmon-fisher, it may, perhaps, be as well not to disclose the exact breeding stations of the species in Scotland, but I should like to give a description of one of the most interesting days I have spent at the haunts of these birds.

The season was late enough to find eggs—it was close on Midsummer's Day, to be precise—when I started out with an old stalker for the high ground. The spring had been arctic, even out of the ordinary, and large fields of the winter's snow still remained on all the higher hills. As we made our way up to the tops, a strong westerly wind brought with it stinging showers of hail, but as we pressed on upwards the wind dropped, and for a short time the sun made his appearance. On our way we crossed the spot where a stalker some years ago had passed his time in digging for Cairngorm stones. I believe that these excavations were successful, and as we passed we found and collected quite a number of crystals of smoked quartz of various sizes and shades of colouring.

Shortly after noon we reached the nesting site of the Dotterel, a plateaux extending for several miles at an elevation of close on 4000 feet above sea-level and devoid of shelter of any kind. Here we had ample evidence of the severity of the past winter and of the absence of any warm weather since, for great fields of snow fringed the precipice which dipped down to the lochan far beneath, and as we commenced our search for the Dotterel the mists descended on the table-land, and snow began to fall in large feathery flakes which soon covered the hill with a uniform white sheet. We imagined that this snowy covering would render easy of discovery any nests of the small Plover which might happen to be in the vicinity, but a careful search was quite unproductive, and we actually saw a flock of a score or so of Dotterel on the most elevated part of the plateau, evidently the whole, or almost the whole, stock of the district. These birds, we took it, had had their eggs destroyed by a heavy storm of snow which swept all the high grounds during the first days of June, and which piled up wreaths of considerable depth in sheltered localities.

A more productive expedition was made on another occasion, when I succeeded in photographing the nest and parent bird. In this instance I came across a nest containing three young birds: two of them had their eyes open and were covered with a healthy growth of down, but the third had evidently been hatched only an hour or so previously, for its eyes were still closed and it had an almost naked appearance, foreign to the young of the *Charadriidæ*. On this occasion, curiously enough, the parents betrayed little anxiety as regards their offspring, but when I visited the hillside three weeks later, and discovered their half-grown chicks, the old birds showed signs of great excitement and an almost complete disregard of my presence. Running backwards and forwards, they frequently uttered their soft and charming whistle, which sounded to me something like " twee, twee, turr," the first two notes being pitched in a high key, the last being a purring sound difficult to put into writing. The head was periodically thrown rapidly back after the completion of the alarm note with a peculiar jerking movement which I have observed in several species of " wading " birds, noticeably the Redshank.

The heat on that particular occasion was intense—a thermometer I had with me showed a temperature of over 80 degrees Fahr. in the shade when placed among the blaeberries and grasses of the hillside—and over each rapidly-diminishing snowfield there hung a small cloud of mist, caused, I imagine, by the great extremes of temperature. This is the only occasion on which I have seen this phenomenon.

An incident not without humour occurred one day when I was on the hills at the end of June with a veteran keeper. The locality was one of the very few where the Dotterel nests comparatively close to civilisation, and although the season was rather too late to find Dotterel still brooding on their eggs, I was hopeful of discovering some of the birds with their families. We searched for some time a likely-looking hill plateau, where, although we saw at least one pair of Dotterel, we could find no indications of young birds, until, having almost abandoned our search as a useless one, we disturbed a Dotterel, which, from her behaviour, gave unmistakable signs that she had young. We decided on remaining quietly, lying full-length on the ground, in the hopes that the young Dotterel would show themselves. Some minutes passed, then first one small bird, closely followed by a second, moved and was marked down. Still we waited for the third member of the family, which, however, failed to put in an appearance, so at length we rose up to photograph the two representatives which we had marked as they crouched.

But as we regained our feet a tragedy was discovered. A small, half-squashed ball of down was revealed lying on the spot which a few seconds previously had supported the keeper. Life still remained in the unfortunate chick, but although I took it back to the keeper's house, where I was quartered, and it was rolled in flannel and placed before the fire, it succumbed to its injuries before the night was out.

The surprise and regret of the old Highlander who had unwittingly been the cause of this tragedy was quite touching, and he assured me that he had " never in his life done such a thing before—no, never."

The two surviving chicks afforded good material for the camera, and while I was photographing them the parent bird, in its anxiety for the welfare of its chicks, ran straight up to under the lens, and attempted to " brood " her two babies within a few feet of where I was standing.

While staying in a well-known forest in Inverness-shire during the summer of 1913, I had opportunities of watching the habits of this bird, which certainly seems, in this particular district at all events, to be holding its own. There have at times been rumours to the effect that egg-hunters have taken up their temporary abode in a small village on the far side of the "march," but the lessee of the forest, who is a keen sportsman and naturalist, and who, unlike the majority of Scottish lairds, spends the summer as well as the autumn months at his shooting lodge, impresses on his stalkers the fact that the high grounds must be carefully watched during June, and that any suspicious person must be covered by the stalking-glass and his movements noted, even if he himself is too far distant to be interrogated.

Our first day on the high tops was unproductive, but on the second occasion we had better luck, for, although we failed to see the birds themselves, we found ample proof of their nesting in the shape of a piece of egg-shell lying on a plateau about 3000 feet above sea-level. During this expedition the cold was intense, though the season was the first week in July, and it was almost impossible to remain for any length of time on the hill-tops. While on our walk to the nesting grounds of the Dotterel, we had an excellent view of an old hill fox. We were descending a steep hill face preparatory to ascending another equally precipitous on the far side of the burn, when I noticed a fox making his way up the opposite hillside. I do not think, judging from his leisurely movements, that he had actually seen us, and as we remained quiet, and half-concealed amongst long heather, Reynard's suspicions gradually became allayed. His progress up the hill

became momentarily slower, until, judging himself out
of danger, he deliberately lay down, curling himself up
like a dog, and fell asleep. Periodically he roused himself and took a survey, without, however, rising to his
feet, yet seemed quite comfortable although a strong and
bitter cold wind was sweeping up the hill and was blowing
straight upon him.

Having discovered undoubted evidence that the
Dotterel was nesting on this hill-top, we took advantage
of the first good day to have a more thorough search
of the ground. A different route was chosen for the
climb. At first our way led along the shores of a deep
hill loch which has yielded many a fine trout and an occasional " ferox " and salmon, and as we started the ascent,
a Golden Eagle was seen to move quickly across the hill
opposite and to sail into the rock, where she had a full-
grown and hungry eaglet awaiting her arrival. At the
edge of the plateau where the Dotterel were nesting, the
ground sloped sharply away to a loch far beneath, and
on this precipitous hillside a pair of Peregrine Falcons
had a family of full-fledged young concealed away in a
chink in a rock.

We were soon rewarded by success, for we had scarcely
reached the highest ground when we saw, moving as
rapidly as they could over the short vegetation, a couple
of young Dotterel. I marked one of these birds down,
but the little fellow sprinted ahead with considerable
speed, and doubled and swerved with such skill that it was
only after covering a good deal of ground that I was able
to capture him. I left him under my cap, and then set
out to catch the second small person. While I was photographing the two Dotterel chicks where I had placed them
together, the parent bird flew around in great distress,
repeatedly whistling in a soft, mournful key, but did not
venture so near as some of the other Dotterel I had ob-

served under similar circumstances. On this occasion only one parent bird was present, and, in fact, it has been my experience that both cock and hen are rarely found in the vicinity of the nest or young.

Curiously enough, it is the male bird which is the smaller and more subdued of the two in colouring, and it is he also, who, it is stated by most observers, hatches out the eggs, and probably also tends the family while his mate is away—perhaps enjoying herself elsewhere. The hen is also said to take the initiative in courtship, though I cannot confirm this from my own personal observations.

The nesting season commences each year at almost precisely the same day, and the young are hatched out about June 22nd. Allowing three weeks as the period of incubation—and I think this is the time as nearly as it has been determined—the first egg must be deposited at the extreme end of May, about a week later than the majority of Ptarmigan commence to lay.

Not the least interesting point in the habits of the Dotterel is the fact that its eggs are always three in number. Now, with all the " waders," a clutch of four is usually deposited. Golden Plover, Green Plover, Curlew, and many others invariably produce four eggs, and I believe the Dotterel is the only representative of the widely-distributed and extensive group to restrict her clutch always to three hostages to fortune.

The eggs are more rounded in shape than is the case with most of the " waders." They are of a light brown ground colour, and are strongly marked, especially at their larger ends, with spots and blotches of rich red brown. In size they are from 1·75 inches to 1·5 inches in length, and from 1·17 inches to 1·1 inches in breadth.

The nest, if such it can be called, is a slight depression scraped out in the hard, peaty ground on some hill plateau, and is sometimes lined with a few pieces of dried grass stems or Alpine lichens, such as *Trichostomum lanugino-sum*. The nest is sometimes partially guarded from the wild storms of wind and rain which prevail at these high levels, by a stone or an irregularity of the ground. Often, however, such shelter is entirely absent, and, like the Ptarmigan, the Dotterel broods on the eggs unprotected from the severity of the weather.

I once watched for some time a pair of Dotterel which were evidently searching for a suitable nesting site. I flushed the birds from the edge of a great field of snow, and so reluctant were they to leave the spot that at first I was almost led to believe they must be nesting in the vicinity, but a search showed me that they could not have eggs at the point where they rose, as the ground had been freed of its covering of snow only a day or two previously. After a short time, during which I remained quiet in the neighbourhood, I could see one of the Dotterel evidently testing likely situations with a view to their suitability as nesting sites. Running actively about, the bird would now and again sit down upon some little knoll, on which it would " brood " in various positions for a few moments, before moving off and going through the same business at another spot. After a time the bird I had under observation flew uphill until it had reached the snow. Here, standing on the surface of the drift, it was a conspicuous object for a while, until it ultimately moved off to some green grass above the snow. We passed the spot again two days later, but the birds were nowhere to be seen.

I shall long remember the magnificent weather conditions we enjoyed during this expedition to the high hills. For three days the sun shone with intense heat, but during the day on which we made the return journey to the low grounds, a strong wind blowing straight from off the distant Atlantic made walking easy. We halted awhile beside the big snowfield : notwithstanding days of tropical weather, the wreath at its centre must have been forty feet deep, and from its lower end a burn of ice-cold water, clear as crystal, was issuing, and was hurrying down the hillside to join itself to the larger stream below. At the edge of the snow, plant life, released a few hours before from its long winter sleep, was as yet brown and apparently devoid of all vitality. A few yards beyond, the delicate blades of grass could be seen forcing their way upwards, and various Alpine ferns pushed forth their fronds, still tightly rolled and brown to the eye. Still farther removed from the region of snow, the hill face was covered with plants showing a soft, pleasing green, and here and there the cushion pink, with its thickly-clustered blooms, tinged the hill with pink ; or the starry saxifrage's snow-white blossom was bathed in the spray of the snow burn. Our view extended to the hills on the western seaboard fifty miles distant, and as we watched we could see the soft grey clouds, carrying with them grateful mist and rain to the parched country, gradually roll in from the great waters, and blot out the hills one by one.

It was some hours later ere they reached our hills, but during their journey over Scotland they had shed their valuable gift of moisture, and here, where the glens were parched and the crops in danger of ruin, only the lightest of showers moistened the thirsty ground. Away from the westerly wind, while the sun still shone, the heat was intense, and as we left the plateau and descended into the corrie known to the hill-man as *Coire Dhoundail*, the scent of countless blaeberry plants was carried up to us on the breeze—that distinctive scent which has such charm, if alone from the memories of the hills which it calls to mind.

To all who know the high grounds the aroma of blae-berry must be a familiar thing, even if he who appreciates it is yet unaware whence it comes. It is a scent, as I have said, of distinction, and a scent which under the influence of a summer's sun is almost overpowering. No other plant has this aroma, but sometimes I think that curious perfume from the flowers of our garden azalea has some resemblance to this essence of the high hills.

I suspect those Dotterel nesting on the highest Scottish plateaux have a nesting season even more precarious and more full of uncertainty than the Ptarmigan. One such plateau which I know well stands nearly 4000 feet above the sea, and almost every season between the end of May and the middle of July a snowstorm of greater or less severity is experienced at this height, the plateau being covered with snow to a depth of a foot or more. There is no doubt that a great number of Dotterel lose their eggs or young every year, yet they seem unwilling to resort to the lower hill-tops. There is only one plateau in Scotland, so far as I know, where a considerable stretch of green grass is met with at the 4000-feet level, and here I saw a solitary representative of the Dotterel family in mid-July 1913.

As is so often the case with the Dotterel, the bird showed reluctance to take wing, this giving cause for suspicions that she had a nest in the neighbourhood, but after a careful search I came to the conclusion that this particular bird was free of family cares, though possibly a snowstorm which swept the hill a week before may have destroyed the eggs or youngsters.

There is extreme grace in the flight of the Dotterel. When an intruder is in the vicinity of her eggs or young— or rather his eggs or young—because, as I have mentioned, it is supposed to be the husband to whom the task of rearing the family is allotted—the bird at times flits restlessly and rapidly across the hill, backwards and forwards, the clean-cut wings moving with swift and powerful

P

strokes only a few feet above the surface of the ground. Sometimes, in its anxiety, the Dotterel flies almost into you before swerving off with soft, whistling cries as it realises its danger.

Although, when they have a family to protect, Dotterel often show quite a noteworthy absence of fear, this is by no means always the case.

On one occasion I came across a couple of broods of young Dotterel on the same hill plateau, about 100 yards distant from each other. The parent in charge of the family I first discovered flew round me in considerable anxiety, but in the second case, although I remained for some time beside one of the chicks—only a few days old, and in such a helpless state that one would have imagined considerable apprehension would have been shown on its behalf—the parent bird remained some little distance off, and, as far as could be seen, showed no great interest in the affairs of its offspring.

It was on a certain day of May that the pair of Dotterel, concerning the family affairs of whom I propose giving an account, and whom I watched closely through the first portion of their duties as parents, arrived on the hill-top. Judging by his more subdued colouring and smaller size, also by the fact that the feathers of his head were brown-tipped, I believe that in this case at all events the male Dotterel carried through unaided the duties of incubation. On June 6th, a day of cold winds and threatening skies, I visited his hill, and had searched for only a few minutes when the Dotterel rose in front of me and, with fluttering and hesitating flight, moved off a few yards before settling and running along the ground. The nest was easy to find. It was the slightest of hollows scraped amongst the short heather, and devoid of lining or decoration of any kind. The eggs, three in number, were strikingly beautiful.

Their ground colour was of a pale olive green, and over this large rich red markings were scattered. It had for a number of years been my ambition to obtain a series of photographs of *An t-amadan mointeach*, and so I decided that, all being well, I would return and attempt to tame this small dweller of the high hills. But almost at once wild weather came to the country of the mountains. The rain was driven across the plateau by a northerly wind, and towards the close of the day snow took its place. For some time the white flakes fell, and then, with the lifting of the clouds, the hill-top stood out in a covering of snow. In the west-facing corries the sun shone with strength sufficient to cause a cloud of grey steam to rise from the ground and to drift away above the sky-line, but on the hill-top the snow remained ; and soon, sharply defined against the white expanse, one saw dark, antlered forms outlined against the grey clouds, for the hill stags came from far across the tops to seek the shelter of the quiet glen beneath. All next day a northerly gale swept the strath. Far below, where the Dotterel sat brooding his eggs, the mist swirled and rushed across the corries, and driving rain and sleet beat in his face. It was not until the afternoon of the second day that the clouds lifted, and from now till the hatching of his young the small bird had fine weather almost uninterruptedly.

It was on a glorious day of mid-June that I next made my way to the Dotterel's country. The air was still, and the sky free of clouds as I passed up the glen. On the burn-side a pair of Sandpipers, the proud possessors of a newly-hatched brood of chicks, showed the most intense anxiety, fluttering before me and uttering plaintive cries. On the loch a brood of young Goosanders were shepherded by their mother, and right on the path a Mallard was brooding a family of well-grown ducklings. In the deep corrie beyond the loch I could see a young Golden Eagle in its eyrie. As I watched through the glass one of the parent Eagles appeared at the nest carrying with it a Grouse for the youngster's morning meal. Soon its mate also alighted on the eyrie, and, while the first bird took its departure, the new-comer commenced to feed its young with the Grouse just brought. Many deer there were in the glen, clustered together at points where the faint breeze could play on them. Even when I reached the plateau, close on three thousand feet above the level of the sea, where the Dotterel had his nesting site, the air was quiet and the heat intense. While I was still quite fifty yards from him the brooding Dotterel rose from his eggs and ran quickly before me in order to decoy me from his nest. I erected the camera a few yards from the nesting place, and took up my position to wait until the bird should become sufficiently bold to return.

Hour after hour I sat there till my legs had lost almost all feeling, and watched the bird gradually approach his treasures. The strong sun, shining full on the un-sheltered nest, warmed his eggs as effectually as he could have done himself, and thus there was no risk of the small unborn chicks perishing of cold. But although the Dotterel was obviously eager to return, he was unable to summon up courage to brave the eye of the camera, and so at length I moved off fifty yards and sat down to watch my unwilling sitter through the glass.

In a very few minutes he hurried back to his nest, sitting down on his eggs and gathering them well to him-self with evident satisfaction, and so I left him for the day —to the hills and to the Tarmachan and to the murmur of the tiny burn which has its birth near the plateau. Next day the sun again shone, but away in the dis-tance great white clouds, massed tier upon tier, foreboded thunder.

In the corrie near the head of the glen a big herd of

stags were feeding on the fresh young grass, and, when they saw me, moved leisurely up on to the sky-line. Through the glass I could see that they had ventured too near the vicinity of the young of a pair of Tarmachan for the liking of those mountain birds. The cock Ptarmigan rose from the ground and, fluttering on ahead of the herd, imagined that he had drawn them from the vicinity of his mate with her chicks. After decoying the stags to what he considered a respectful distance, he flew back to the vicinity of his mate, congratulating himself that she and the young had escaped danger. In the strong sunlight one could almost see the hill grass shooting, and from the young foliage of the blaeberry plants the air was filled with perfume. Near many a small hill streamlet—such a streamlet is known as *feith* in the poetical language of the Gael—the blossoms of the starry saxifrage were opening their white petals with that characteristic yellow spot at the base of each. The yellow saxifrage (*Saxifraga azoides*) and *Saxifraga hypnoides* were also noted and admired, while on the edge of the plateau the mountain azalea spread forth its delicate china-like flowers of pink from trailing, prostrate stems.

The behaviour of the Dotterel was on this occasion different to when last I had visited him, for he allowed me to erect the camera six feet from the nest without abandoning his eggs. I left the camera with its eye pointing full at him and retired a few yards. He remained without movement for a time. Then, to my surprise, and for no apparent reason, he rose from his nest and fluttered away.

Again I waited near for the greater part of the day in the hopes that he would return to his nest. I marked the storms gathering in various parts of the wide area seen from this hill plateau. Away to the north the Monadh Liath Mountains, at first clearly defined, and with the sun shining full on their snow-flecked corries, gradually became obscured by dark rain clouds. Over Ben Alder, to the west, a second storm gathered, and southwards, over Atholl, a cloud black as night wrapped hill and glen. Overhead, in the small opening of blue sky being rapidly encroached upon by these three storms, the sun still shone brilliantly. And now, toward the south-west there shot across the inky clouds brilliant flashes of lightning, and the dull roll of the thunder was borne across to me. Gradually, almost imperceptibly, the storm from Atholl approached. The Dotterel, growing bolder than on my previous visits, slipped on to his nest just as the first drops of rain touched the dry vegetation of the plateau. A few moments more, and a deluge of water descended on the hill, quickly drenching me to the skin. Such was the force of the raindrops that they rebounded from the ground, and every dry and disused water-course was filled. But as I made my way down to the glen beneath I realised how clearly defined were the limits of this tropical downpour, for a mile to the northward the ground was scarcely damp, though here, too, with the lengthening of the evening, there descended another storm. Before night it, too, had disappeared, and the sky held many fleecy clouds which were turned to rose by the light of the setting sun.

On the morrow I again visited the Dotterel. Again the sun shone, and now I became aware of the great change there had been wrought among the hill faces during the past few days ; for everywhere one saw fresh green grass, and on some hillsides many plants of broom —eaten to the ground almost by the stags—added a golden note. The Dotterel left his nest as I appeared, and again there ensued a long wait for him to return. It was, I think, on this occasion that he first broke his silence, uttering that charmingly soft whistle of his as

he ran round me restlessly. As it was necessary for me
to remain without movement, I was unable to follow him
when he moved behind me, and after a time I heard him
—so I thought—utter a curious, almost human, cry of
distress, quite unlike anything I had ever before known.
I resolved to place it on record, although I felt doubtful
whether I should be believed.

After a while, in order to change my cramped position,
I moved round, and, to my astonishment, found a young
deer calf nestling up against me. The small person was
quite without fear, and as I had no wish to move farther
than necessary, I resumed my watching, with my curious
companion sheltering against me.

It was not until I rose in order to change the plate
that the small calf realised how unhappy and lonely he
was, for he rose unsteadily to his feet and called piteously
several times. He wanted his milk very much indeed,
and endeavoured to obtain it, first from me and then from
the camera. He offered an excellent subject for a photograph, but it was none too easy to secure one, for he
insisted on following me everywhere. And so I carried
him away across the plateau and set him down on a
soft, grassy slope a couple of hundred yards distant, never
doubting but that his mother would return shortly to
search for him.

I was successful this day in obtaining a number of
photographs of the Dotterel, and with the dipping of the
sun behind the clouds of a great thunderstorm I moved
off to search the hill for another nest. In this I was unsuccessful, though I flushed a Dotterel—I imagine she was
the mate of my own acquaintance—near a little cairn,
a few hundred yards from the nest.

Towards evening I left the hill, and believing that all
must be well, passed by the place where I had placed
the small calf, for earlier in the afternoon I had seen

a hind cross the plateau behind me and make straight for the spot where the calf was left.

But during these hours a small life had been lost, and a small spirit of life had gone out into the great spaces, beyond where our knowledge may carry us. He had not been dead long, this little calf His body was still warm, and his tongue hung pathetically from the corner of his mouth. But of his mother there was no sign ; she was probably a young hind, and young hinds are without experience as mothers, and at times desert their offspring after birth.

As I crossed the hill the sky lighted westward with the passing of the storm, and Ben Nevis stood outlined, with its snowy corries and its great precipices—a barrier stationed against the strong storms of the Atlantic.

It was on June 23rd that the young Dotterel chicks commenced to cry out feebly inside their prisons, and to tap vigorously on the shells as they forced their way out into the world. On this morning the air was of extraordinary clearness. Eastwards the Cairngorm range of hills stood sharply out. The big snowfield on Horseman's Corrie of Braeriach was clear, and the flat top of Cairn Toul, with the snow wreaths at the head of the Tailor's Corrie of Ben Mac Dhui lying behind it, caught the rays of the sun. South, the view extended as far as the hills of distant Kinross, and north-west every snow-bed on the Knoidart Hills was distinct.

The air was cold, and soon a squall of wind and rain swept across Scotland from north to south. The temperature fell rapidly, so that, even with the sun shining full on the plateau where I lay, the air was sharp and without warmth. In the midst of the squall an Eagle soared grimly past, making for his eyrie away to the north, but the Dotterel apparently did not see him—at all events, he continued to run restlessly round his nest. With the passing of the squall the sun again shone out, and a solar halo of exceptional dimensions was formed, the sun's rays striking with prismatic effect on the many ice particles in suspension in the upper air.

When disturbed the behaviour of the Dotterel was interesting. He at first declined to approach near to the camera, running actively round in circles, and feeding on the many insects that the hill-top harboured. His sense of hearing must have been extremely acute, for he several times stopped suddenly, then, retracing his steps, picked up some small insect which he had heard after he had passed. Once a large beetle settled near him. He ran up, pecked at the creature, but missed his mark, and the beetle took wing, alighting again, however, a few yards in front of him. Again the Dotterel essayed to pick up the insect, but again was unsuccessful. This time he did not pursue the fugitive. He ran over the heather with great speed, with head bent forward. Once he tripped and nearly lost his balance on a piece of heather, but, seeing that he did not look where he was going, he was singularly steady on his feet. After an hour or so his circles gradually narrowed, and he evidently debated whether he could venture on to his nest with the inscrutable eye of the camera fixed full upon him. Time after time he approached to within a few feet of his nest. Then his courage failed him, and he endeavoured charmingly to decoy the camera from his eggs, trailing his wings and spreading his tail wide in his effort. Sometimes he would pretend to brood on a nest near, constantly rising, when he saw the camera could not be lured on, and almost at once crouching motionless in a different position.

Again, at other times, having approached very near the danger zone, an idea seemed to strike him, and turning about he ran rapidly away until he was sometimes out of sight. But evidently he was consumed with anxiety when away from his home, for a minute or two afterwards I could see him running at top speed back towards his nest. His soft whistle he uttered only when he was very near to me, and on one occasion he moved off a few feet, and turning towards the hill-top where I had seen his mate, whistled three times with a note quite distinctive from his usual cry, and as near as it can be put in writing, sounding like " pēēu, pēēu, pēēu." His mate was either indifferent, or more probably was out of range at the time, for during all my visits to the nest I did not once see her or hear her near.   Sometimes I retreated, and allowed the Dotterel to return to the nest for the space of half an hour or so.

After he had become more or less used to my presence, he was in the habit of sitting very close after such an absence on my part, so that I was able on one occasion to approach to within a very few feet without causing him to leave.   When, however, his nervousness was such that he was unable to remain at his post longer, he jumped from his nest and dragged himself along the ground in a crouching position with his tail spread to its greatest extent and his wings beating the heather.   He uttered the while plaintive cries—not whistles—which were sufficiently distressed to move even the most stony-hearted.

I had ample opportunities of observing his beautiful plumage during my long waits.   On the crown of his head the feathers—black at a distance—were seen to be in reality of a very dark chocolate brown.   His ash-grey neck and upper breast were bounded by a strongly-marked line of white with an irregular margin of black feathers, and the lower part of his breast was of a warm red brown tint.   On his back the feathers were tawny, each margined with white.   Sometimes as he ran the wind blew his tail feathers almost over his back, with curious effect.

After many attempts, when he faltered and turned away when only a few inches from the nest, the Dotterel at length settled down on his eggs with the camera staring full at him, at once crouching low and arranging his eggs beneath him with the movement characteristic of all birds when brooding. But after a minute or two he became restless. Several times in quick succession he opened and closed his bill, then moved his head and discarded his crouching attitude. Perhaps he realised that he had warmed up his eggs sufficiently for them to withstand a further period of exposure, for he then jumped up and ran from the nesting site; but he soon returned, and again brooded his eggs.

That day two of the eggs were chipped, and twenty-four hours later I again visited the Dotterel, expecting to find young in the nest. The father bird was sitting remarkably lightly, considering the critical period of his brooding, and, although the two chicks were still actively hammering against the walls of their prisons, they had progressed little farther in their process of freeing themselves. In the third egg there was as yet no sign of life.

This time I did not attempt to photograph the Dotterel at first, but moved on across the hill, and soon I saw him hurry back to his nest and settle down upon it. For a time I left him, and on my return found him sitting very closely indeed. Even when disturbed he moved only a short distance, and soon returned.

The day was without sun, and with mist on the tops, while a cold wind crossed the plateau from the west. I noted that the Dotterel, although approaching his eggs down wind, turned about abruptly as he settled down in order to brood facing the breeze. It was curious that the female bird was nowhere to be seen, although I searched the greater part of the hill.

The next day saw a westerly gale, bringing with it cold rain squalls, with, I believe, snow on the highest ground. Under such conditions I was reluctant to disturb the Dotterel, and so it was not until the following day that I made my way for the last time up the glen leading to his hill. A strong breeze still shook the birches in the glen, but the sun was shining clearly. Again I watched the eaglet for a time on my way and saw him flapping his white wings in the strong light. Blue Hares rose in front of me and shot away at great speed, though curiosity soon mastered alarm, and they sat up on their hind legs to watch the unexpected visitor. A Grouse with her brood displayed considerable boldness in her anxiety for her young, and the air was filled with the twitterings of Meadow Pipits, most of them with young families in the neighbourhood.

As I neared the nest there was no sign of the Dotterel, and, to my disappointment, I discovered that the nest contained only the single egg which had been without signs of life two days before. Forty yards away I found a portion of one of the shells where it had been carried by the parent bird, but of him and his family there were no signs.

For several hours I searched for the brood, visiting the more sheltered hollows, and the clear springs at the head of the corrie, in the hopes that he might have led down his young to drink. But of them there was no sign. An old cock Ptarmigan scrambled along amongst some rough ground at my feet before flying off, croaking, and unwilling to leave his mate. Above their nesting rock the Peregrines circled, rising together into the breeze with quick motions of their strong wings. Across the loch beneath the breeze rushed, throwing up white-capped wavelets on which the sun shone brilliantly. In the green corrie a number of hinds were feeding, and with them a solitary calf only a day or two old. He was prettily marked with dark spots, and his small tail was of a light fawn colour, contrasting markedly with the rest of his coat. He was the only youngster amongst the herd, and he often approached too near the various hinds to whom he did not belong, being driven off with scant sympathy to his rightful parent. Somewhere near the Dotterel was shelter- ing his newly-hatched young, and in the midst of such wild surroundings I left him to his well-earned quietness and rest.

An interesting fact in the nesting of the Dotterel is that it scarcely ever takes wing from the vicinity of the nest and young, but when it spies the approach of the human intruder, runs forward over the short Alpine vegetation with considerable speed, in order to place as great a distance as possible between itself and its treasures before being noticed. If on these occasions one lies quite still for a few minutes, the fugitive gathers together a certain amount of courage, and gradually makes its way back, until it is standing inquiringly only a few yards distant. At such times the white stripe which extends from above the eye to the back of the head is clearly marked, and at once serves to identify the bird from the Golden Plover, though the latter bird is also of considerably stronger and heavier build.

Numerous instances are on record of Dotterel having broods of young in late July or even August—a keeper of my acquaintance found a bird sitting on eggs on July 26th—but I think that the birds rarely nest again if their first clutches are destroyed by snow in early June. Should the first hatching have been successful, the young Dotterel are able to take wing before the end of July, and shortly after this date the birds, young and old, collect into large flocks preparatory to the southern migration. Its journey south is a more leisurely affair than its spring flight to its nesting haunts, and it is not till November and December that it crosses the Mediterranean at Malta.

A few birds remain through the winter on the northern shores of this sea, and large flocks winter in the hill country of Southern Palestine. Through south-west Turkestan it passes on migration and winters in Persia. At this season it is also seen in Egypt and along the shores of the Red Sea. Even in the wastes of the Sahara the Dotterel is seen, but is not found east of the Himalayas or south of the Equator.

On migration they pass regularly through Italy, France, and all parts of Germany. It is interesting, however, to realise that those moving over France have nested in Norway and Lapland, while those which have bred on the steppes of Russia and Western Siberia travel south by way of Turkey and the Crimea.

There is a certain consolation in the fact that, even if the Dotterel should be temporarily banished from this country as a nesting species, it will have no difficulty in re-establishing itself should favourable opportunities occur, for it is a fairly abundant nesting species on the tundras beyond forest growth from the Atlantic to the Pacific.

A few, I believe, remain to nest on the higher peaks of the Alps, but generally its line of flight during the spring migration takes it much farther north.

It has not been met with in the Faroes nor, curiously enough, in Iceland or Greenland, though it might be imagined that many suitable nesting sites would be found in the latter countries. It may be, however, that the Dotterel will yet be found to be a summer migrant to these parts. It breeds in the northern districts of Scandinavia, also in north Norway and Swedish Lapland, but in Finland is found only in the extreme northern extremity. Still, I think, it is most numerous amongst the tundras of Siberia, where it arrives sometimes before the winter's snows have been dispersed by the sun's heat ; but, so far as I am informed, it does not nest east of the water-shed between the Yenesei and Lena Rivers. During its southern migration the Dotterel makes a stay of a few days at various localities along our coast-line. To many of these visitors man is quite unknown, and their confidence in his good intentions often leads to their destruction.

In olden days five or six sportsmen used to go out to a spot which Dotterel frequented, and having discovered the birds, stretched a net at some distance beyond them. Then they advanced slowly and without sound, throwing small sticks or stones to arouse the birds from their dozing. These fowlers firmly believed that the birds mimicked whatever they saw, and thus attempted to amuse them by extending a leg or arm. By such manœuvres the flock were gradually guided to the spot where the net was ready to receive them. As Dotterel made excellent eating, the fowlers went to considerable trouble to obtain a good haul of birds.

Since the female Dotterel is the more brightly-coloured of the two, it may be as well to give a detailed description of her. The general colour of the upper parts is pale grey-ish brown, this brown being darker on the wings and tail. The shaft of the first primary is white, and the outer tail feathers are broadly tipped with white. Wing coverts, innermost secondaries, and scapulars edged with rich buff. Crown and back of the head bluish black ; from above the eye two white stripes extend, one over each eye, and join together on the nape. Chin and upper throat white ; cheeks and ear coverts white, spotted with dark brown. The greyish brown of the back extends round the neck across the breast, where it suddenly ends in a white band faintly margined above and below with black. The under parts below the breast are rich chestnut, shading into nearly black on the belly. The thighs, vent, and under tail coverts are nearly white. Axillaries and under wing coverts are pale grey. Bill black, legs and feet dull yellowish brown, claws black, irides hazel.

The male differs from the female in having the black feathers of the head and brown grey feathers of the mantle margined with buff. In his case also the black on the belly is somewhat less developed.

The female Dotterel weighs from 5 to $5\frac{1}{2}$ ounces, the male only 4 ounces. The length is about 9 inches.

THE OYSTER CATCHER

HÆMATOPUS OSTRALEGUS

TRILLEACHAN, GILLE-BRIGHDE, GILLE-BRIDEIN (*Gaelic*); HÔITRIER
PIE (*French*); AUSTERNFISCHER (*German*).

A CURIOUS and quite misplaced name has been given to
this handsome bird, and it would be not a little instructive
to discover the origin of its cognomen. As far as I know,
the diet of the Oyster Catcher never embraces an oyster,
and the Irish name given to this bird—that of Mussel
Picker—is decidedly more appropriate.

Like another Highland bird, the Common Gull, the
Oyster Catcher would seem to have two distinct habits,
according to the coasts it frequents. On the west coast-line
of Scotland it is found nesting in considerable numbers,
but along the eastern seaboard—at all events, along those
parts with which I am familiar—it is only as a winter
visitor that the Mussel Picker is known. Early in March
the birds leave the river estuaries, and make their way
in pairs up the rivers, moving in easy stages of only a few
miles each day, and marking time should wintry weather
be experienced. Along the rivers Dee and Spey the
Oyster Catcher is found in considerable numbers. On
the Dee it nests four miles from the estuary, and thence
up to a point ten miles west of Braemar and, by river,
close on eighty miles from the North Sea. In like
manner it frequents the Spey and its tributaries almost
to their sources. For instance, in the Forest of Gaick
it is numerous on the flat between Loch an t-Seilich and
Loch Bhrotain, 1500 feet above sea-level. Above this

elevation I have never met with it either nesting or as a migrant.

A month after their arrival at their nesting sites the Oyster Catchers commence to construct their nests. Usually these consist merely of shallow depressions scraped in the shingle fringing a river or hill stream, and are devoid of lining or decoration of any sort. Sometimes the dried droppings of rabbits are collected and are used as a floor to the nest. At times, however, an Oyster Catcher, more ambitious or energetic than her neighbours, gathers together quite a bulky collection of dead heather stems, and constructs a nest in the true sense of the term.

Flat stretches of heather-clad ground adjoining a river would seem to be well liked by the Oyster Catcher as nesting-grounds, but often the nest is at a considerable distance from any water. Two instances came to my notice recently of an Oyster Catcher choosing as a nesting site a field of young oats.

The eggs of this handsome bird usually number three. They are less pyriform than is generally the case with the family of waders, and are large for the size of the bird. Light brown in their ground colour, they are spotted or streaked with spots of dark grey-brown. The birds never sit closely even when their young are on the point of hatching. On the approach of danger they sometimes fly straight off the nest or sometimes run as fast as they can for some distance before taking wing—it depends on the individual, I think. They usually leave in silence, but if one remains too long at their nesting site, and the birds begin to have fears lest their eggs are becoming too cold, they then fly restlessly round, uttering an occasional cry. But with the hatching out of their brood their anxiety increases a thousandfold, and the birds fly round the " danger zone " uttering shrill excited cries repeatedly ; there are, in fact, few members of the bird world which

betray so much solicitude on behalf of their families.
Nesting as they do on the banks of burns and rivers,
floods during the month of May not infrequently play
havoc with the eggs of the Mussel Pickers. In the Dee
valley the spate of 1913 must have washed away thousands
of their eggs, and an equal amount of damage was done
on the Spey and its tributaries in 1914.   Though the latter
spate was experienced as early as the first week in May,
very few of the birds laid second clutches of eggs, and
were seen consorting together either in pairs or in small
companies.

The Oyster Catchers of the Farne Islands, on the other
hand, would appear to be more determined to rear a family
than their relations of the Spey valley, for as late as
August I have seen them still brooding on eggs.

During the nesting season the Mussel Pickers are the
most restless of birds, and what sleep they require is
snatched at odd moments throughout the day.   Through
the whole of the short June night the birds may be heard
calling restlessly from some frequented spot near the river,
or the regular cries of an individual flying unseen overhead carry far across the glen, wrapped in deep twilight.

During the nesting season the Oyster Catchers are
sociable birds, and it is rare to find a pair nesting quite by
themselves.   A favourite site is an island in midstream
on which grows short heather intermixed with pebbles.
Here a number of birds may be nesting in a comparatively
small area.   They are quite sensible to the fact that the
river is a barrier to any intruder, and they rarely leave
their nests if a person walks along the river-bank only
fifty yards or so distant.

One of the most curious nesting-places of an Oyster
Catcher was the permanent way of the Highland Railway, the bird laying her eggs actually between one set of
metals.   A train passing at full speed over the adjoining set

failed to cause her to leave her nest, but she moved off just before a train passed over her own line. This remarkable nesting station was chosen at least two years in succession.

I have seen an Oyster Catcher sitting on her eggs in a larch wood, and the nest has also been found on the top of a pine-stump. Before the full complement of eggs has been laid, both cock and hen remain a short distance from the nest to guard their future young.

Incubation is a lengthy process with the Oyster Catcher, for the bird broods close on a month before her eggs hatch out. Even after the young have chipped the hard shell a period of quite forty-eight hours may elapse before they are able to emerge.

A curious and distinctive method of flight indulged in by the Oyster Catcher during the nesting season has not, so far as I am aware, been put on record. I am unable to state definitely that it is the song of the male bird, but incline to that belief. In the normal flight of the Oyster Catcher, it should be stated, the wings are moved with great rapidity, but not infrequently a certain bird, with no apparent reason, abruptly changes his flight to slow wing beats, comparable to those of a gull. With each thrust of his wings he gives utterance to a cry more long drawn out than the usual whistle, sounding like " kobeeak, kobeeak." When this particular call is heard it is quite certain that the bird has altered his flight. Sometimes, after flying for a few minutes or even less in this fashion, the song—as I imagine it to be—is ceased, and the normal flight straightway resumed.

Often the Oyster Catcher flies only a few inches above the surface of a river, but when a bridge has to be passed the birds never, so far as my experience goes, move under it, though they have to rise quite a considerable distance to surmount the obstacle.

Often when a number of Mussel Pickers are together

they indulge in what appears to be a game. With their heads bent low and their handsome red bills almost touching the ground, the birds follow a leader quickly over the shingle, giving utterance all the while to sharp whistling cries. Sometimes after a burst of calling the birds rise in a body and fly off, still whistling to each other. At their summer haunts the food of the Oyster Catcher consists largely of worms, the birds visiting the fields near their nesting site, especially after rain. The young would appear to be fed on worms also, for I have seen an Oyster Catcher making its way rapidly to its nesting ground, and bearing in its bill a worm of great size, which dangled earthwards for all the world like a small snake. Though most demonstrative of birds when the safety of its young is concerned, the Oyster Catcher rarely attacks other birds venturing near its nest : a passing Hoodie or Gull is left in peace, though, should a solitary Green Plover be nesting anywhere near, she dashes out with no hesitation and swoops repeatedly at the stranger, which was ignored by the Mussel Picker, driving it determinedly far beyond her nesting-ground. It is July before the young Oyster Catchers are strong on the wing, and by August the majority of the birds, young and old, take their departure from their nesting-grounds, appearing about this time on the river estuaries along the coasts. It is doubtful, however, whether the individuals which pass the autumn and winter months with us are the birds which have nested along the rivers of the same district, for it is probable that a south migration, even if only of a few score of miles, takes place at the fall of the year.

During the winter months the Oyster Catcher is one of the most prominent of our shore-feeding birds. Immediately the tide has receded sufficiently to leave exposed the highest lying of the mudflats, Mussel Pickers appear on the scene, and at once commence to search for food, mussels being favourite morsels. The birds feed by night as well as during the day : it depends entirely on the state of the tide.

Northward of our Islands the Oyster Catcher breeds in the Faroes and plentifully in Scandinavia. It is also found in Ireland, and even as far north as Archangel. During the winter migration it is found in Africa, and extends as far as India.

Description.—The bill is long and blunt, coloured of a beautiful and striking red. Head, neck, mantle, and wings black. The lower back, rump, and basal half of the tail white. Breast and abdomen white. Median and major wing coverts white. Legs and feet pale yellow. After the autumn moult a band of white extends backwards from the chin to join a broad white band reaching from the ear coverts across the throat. The full-fledged young have the greater wing coverts, innermost secondaries and scapulars with pale margins. The longest upper tail coverts are barred across the tips with black and buff. The downy young are pale brown above mottled with grey. On the crown is a black patch. Along the back run two longitudinal stripes of black, and a loop of black is present at the hinder end of the body. The under parts are white.

On one occasion I observed an almost pure white Oyster Catcher in a certain glen. The bird appeared to be one of a pair nesting near, but its abnormal colour evidently rendered it distasteful to the other birds of its species, for they were inclined to pursue it when it appeared.

THE SNOW BUNTING

PLECTROPHENAX NIVALIS

GEALAG 'N T'SNEACHDAIDH, GEALAG-AN-T-SNEACHD, EUN AN-T-SNEACHDA
(*Gaelic*); PODOROSCHNIK (*Russian*); ORLOTAN DE NIEGE (*French*);
SCHNEEAMMER (*German*); SNJÓTITLINGUR = SNOW TWITTERER (*Icelandic*); SNAAFOOL (*Shetland*).

EVEN more than the Ptarmigan is the Snow Bunting a
dweller of the remote and desolate mountain lands, where
there is silence always. The snow-bird makes its home
amongst the great masses of granite scree where is an
entire absence of vegetation, and over which fierce winds
sweep so often, even during the finest season of the year.
On only the very highest of our Scottish hills is the Snow
Bunting to be found during the season of its nesting.
Whereas the Tarmachan rarely hatches off her brood
above the 3500 foot line, I have never known the Snow
Bird to be seen below this level during the months of
summer; and during those bright and sunny days, when
even on the huge hills the air is still, I have heard him
in full song above the 4000-foot level.

There is a certain glen, buried deep amongst the big
hills, and at its highest point, almost 4000 feet in elevation,
where the Snow Bunting for years nested in security.
Many days of pleasant memory have I spent there with
the small people as my companions. It was in the very
early hours of the morning of a July day that I reached
the cairn of the precipitous hill guarding the glen to the
east. A west wind brought with it soft filmy mist-clouds,
which sped softly over the hill-top, hiding the first rays of
the sun and blotting out all distant view. But at the head

of the glen the air was clear, and there was brought up
to me with the breath of the wind the clear musical notes
of the Snow Bird's song. The songster was perched on
the top of a boulder, and he had not repeated his song
many times before he flew down and commenced to pick
up craneflies or " daddy long legs," which are so numerous
on the high hills during the season of early summer.
Having procured a number of these insects, the bird now
flew a short distance to where one of his brood was concealed, and proceeded to feed the expectant youngster.
When I arrived at the spot both birds showed signs of
great anxiety, and the hen fed her young almost under my
feet, endeavouring afterwards to induce it to take wing with
her. But the youngster had evidently left the nest only
a short time before, and was unable to fly more than a
few yards before its feeble wings refused to carry it farther,
and it lighted once more amongst the stones. During
that one July morning of 1909 I had under observation
no fewer than four pairs of Snow Buntings—two with
their young—in this wild glen.

For several years afterwards the corrie welcomed its
Snow Birds with the coming of each spring, but in decreasing numbers. And then one year a tragedy—
regrettable, I venture to think, and avoidable—befell
one of the families. A collector, searching the high hills,
discovered the remote corrie and was attracted by the
song of the cock. He was fortunate enough to discover
the nest, and in course of time killed both the parent birds
and removed the nest and eggs. And now, for three years
at least, the song of the Snow Bird is no more heard in the
glen. On days when the sun lighted up the corrie, and
when the air was quiet, I have visited the former haunt
of the Snow Birds, and have sat and waited long amongst
the great stones where the birds formerly sang. But
there has been silence—a silence complete save for the

THE CORRIE OF THE SNOW BUNTING.

occasional call of a Wheatear, or the murmuring of the
burn as it threads its way southward, with the summer's
sun reflected back from its waters of wonderful clearness.

One sees many a hill and glen from the country of the
Snow Bunting. Sometimes, away on the western hills,
the mist has lain thick while here the weather was fine
and clear. Sometimes, too, after a dawn of mist and wind,
the air has suddenly been stilled, and the hills one by one
have shown themselves out of the mist sea.

Once when I was listening for the Snow Bird's song,
a remarkable change in the weather was, with scarce
any warning, experienced through the whole of Scotland.
The morning was beautifully fine, scarce a breath of wind
stirred, and the sun shone full on the scree where was the
Snow Bunting's home. But soon a curious layer of grey
cloud overspread the sky. The clouds were at an immense
height, and scarcely dimmed the rays of the sun ; and
even on Ben Nevis, fifty miles distant, every snowfield
stood out distinctly. Away north-westward, at an even
greater distance, the hills of the far north-west—of
Knoidart and of the district bordering on Skye—were
plentifully sprinkled with the snow of a winter which was
now long since passed.

Within the space of less than an hour a rapidly advancing depression held the whole of the vast area in its
grip. Hill after hill was rapidly dimmed, first in a thin
rain, and then, as the storm gathered, in cold grey mist-
clouds. The wind increased to almost gale force, driving
before it stinging blasts of rain and forcing the clouds low
down on the faces of the hills so recently bathed in bright
sunlight. A great darkness settled on the country of the
glens. Lower and lower the clouds were driven.

One hill in particular presented a curiously grand,
arresting appearance. At times it was free of clouds,
from base to summit. Then, in the course of a few

seconds a great cloud was formed on its sheltered face.
Increasing quickly in size, the cloud canopy blotted out
the hill, until, on reaching the summit, it felt the full
force of the gale and was hurried for miles to leeward,
appearing as an immense column of smoke rolling northward down the glen.

On more than one occasion I have made my way to
the remote glen of the Snow Birds during the hours of
twilight—there is no night on the Scottish hills at midsummer—and have listened for the first song of the
Bunting with the strengthening of the dawn.

Once the sky was covered with heavy thundery clouds
during this midnight walk, and the moon shone fitfully
and without power. Not a breath of wind moved in the
glen. From time to time Tarmachan that I disturbed
threw out their croaking calls of alarm into the night,
or shadowy forms of stags moved past. An hour and five
minutes after midnight the Snow Bunting commenced
his song. He was on his favourite field of granite scree,
at a height of close on 4000 feet above sea-level, and he
sang with power and almost incessantly till seven o'clock.
The weather up to this time has been brilliantly fine.
Above the glen the sky was deep clear blue, and only near
the lochan lying nearly 1000 feet beneath us was a cloud
lingering. Many times did the westerly breeze cross the
lochan, and, gently lifting the cloud, attempt to bear it
down the glen, but it persistently remained ; and then, as
the morning grew older, the wind shifted to the east, and
gradually a white bank of billowy mist slipped quietly
up the big glen, blotting out all the land beneath us. For
some time yet the hill remained clear in the sunlight,
then with the advance of the cloud there ensued a struggle
between the strong rays of the sun and the mist-pall,
before the latter ultimately shrouded even the highest
tops and the sun was finally obscured.

A few days later I again visited the glen of the Snow Bunting. On this occasion the heat was intense, and the songster was silent. I looked for him with no success, till at last I discovered him in the vicinity of a rapidly dwindling snowfield, where he had sought some relief from the unusually high temperature then prevailing. At times he would walk out on to the snow's surface, feeding on the insects which are always to be found on snowfields on the high hills during the summer months, and would seek to cool himself by running over the snow with his head half buried beneath the surface, and throwing up a furrow as from a diminutive snow-plough. Occasionally he would sing snatches from his song, but did not return to the scree, where he was usually to be found, until late in the afternoon.

Associated as it always is with the grandest and most inspiring surroundings, the song of the Snow Bunting has had for me a peculiar fascination ; and even if heard where there were other and more recognised song-birds to compete, I still think that it would arrest attention. It is powerful, and can be heard at a great distance ; but it is singularly elusive, and sometimes it is a matter of considerable difficulty to locate the songster, the notes appearing to come now from one part of the hill, now from another. It would almost seem as though the bird had the power of ventriloquy, though the apparent elusiveness of the song is due more, I think, to the fact that the songster in his excitement moves himself about, so that he faces different points, and also that currents of air are usually moving over the hills in various directions. The notes of the Snow Bird are clear and flute-like, but individual birds vary, and some have more striking songs than others. Commencing in a low key, the notes—five or six in number—rapidly rise until the bird throws out a strong, clear whistle, which at a distance is the only part of the song audible. This whistle may constitute the final note of the song, or the bird may finish his effort with a series of quickly uttered and confused notes. So far as my experience goes the song is never, except during wild and stormy weather, uttered on the ground, the point of vantage being a boulder on the scree near where the hen is brooding on her eggs.

A Snow Bunting usually has several singing stations that he visits in turn, and on the favourite of these he spends the most of his time. Even at a considerable distance he can be picked up through the glass, for in size he is larger than a chaffinch, and his strikingly handsome plumage of black and white renders him a conspicuous object. I have seen a Snow Bunting, after having sung for a considerable time, fly out into the air, and with strong flight make his way to the far side of the glen, there presumably to continue his singing. At times, too, he will fly up into the air much in the fashion of the Tree Pipit, and, with wings spread V-shape, sail back to his boulder uttering his song.

Once, while watching a Snow Bunting through the glass, I saw him suddenly rise from the scree and dash backward and forward in a most curious and erratic manner before moving off to a farther part of the hillside, where, I imagine, his mate must have been sitting. In contrast to those of his tribe which are seen in our glens at the approach of winter, the Snow Bunting at his nesting-ground is a singularly confiding bird, and will allow the ornithologist to stalk him to within a few yards without leaving his singing-station. One season, having noted that a certain individual bird invariably spent the greater part of his time singing from a little moss-covered knoll, I erected my camera a few feet off, covered it with stones, and, having attached 100 feet of tubing to it, moved a short distance away in the hope that the bird

would return and that I might obtain a photograph of
him. But he apparently noticed that his singing-station
had been altered : at all events he did not return to it.
Later in the afternoon, when my companion and I were
lying half asleep in the hot sun, the songster suddenly
appeared and commenced to sing only a few yards from
us. My large camera being unavailable, I stalked the
Snow Bunting with a kodak that I had with me, and succeeded in obtaining a photograph of the bird in the middle
of its song at short range.

Toward the second week of July the snow-bird utters
his song less frequently, also he extends his range and
moves out on to the highest hill-tops during fine calm
weather. By August, save in exceptional cases, he is
silent.

The nest of the Snow Bunting is placed where it is
almost impossible of discovery, unless the parent birds
are marked down as they visit it either with building
materials or with food for their young. It is built hidden
away amongst the stones, at a depth maybe of well
over a foot, and the hen-bird does not usually take wing
until actually compelled to do so. The eggs number from
five to as many as eight. Their ground colour is of a
bluish green, and they are spotted and blotched with
rich reddish brown, finely striated with deep blackish
brown.

In size they vary from 1·05 to 8·2 inch in length,
and from ·67 to ·60 inch in breadth. They repose on a
lining of dried grass-stems and Ptarmigan feathers. The
building of the nest is commenced almost with the melting
of the snows—about May 20th—and the hen begins
to brood during the first week in June. The young are
fed mainly on insects, and both parent birds share in
these duties, the cock varying the monotony of searching
for delicacies with snatches of his song. By the first days

of July the young have left the nest. They lack the colouring of their parents, for they are of a uniform brown colour, and harmonise closely with the boulders where they are found. Often the eggs, either from cold or from some other cause, become useless, and in such cases second broods are sometimes, but rarely I think, reared. Eggs have been found in the Shetlands as late as July 2. From the time the hen commences to brood till the young are able to leave the nest a period of just over four weeks elapses.

As there is usually an absence of water as well as of vegetation where the Snow Bunting nests, the young broods, when sufficiently strong on the wing, are led down the hill by their parents till they reach some spring or burn, and remain more or less in its vicinity afterwards. When a cold and strong wind sweeps over the hill, young and old crawl into the cracks and chinks between the boulders, and remain almost dormant, without food, till summer again comes to the hills. It is consequently of little use to search even a favourite haunt for the Snow Bunting unless the conditions are favourable, for in all probability there will be no sign of their presence. I have seen a young bird, sheltering in this manner, experience considerable difficulty in gaining the open as I passed.

Though I imagine that, owing to the sheltered character of their nesting situations, the snowstorms which so often sweep the high hills during June should not cause the hen to desert her eggs, I have frequently seen pairs of birds during July which had no broods with them, and which were not, so far as I could determine, engaged in nesting. And yet their enemies are few. The hill-fox I have seen at their wild country. He was basking in the clear sunlight of an early June morning, after, maybe, a successful stalk during the hours of darkness, when he captured a hen Ptarmigan as she brooded on her nest. The stoat is sometimes present, but he usually confines his attentions to the lower end of the glen. The eagle, which sails so proudly over the hill-top, has no eye for the Snow Bunting, and the Peregrine rarely visits the glen.

I have wondered, sometimes, whether the Snow Bird noticed, as he sang his song with only a few seconds of interval through the long summer day, the grand panorama of mountain and glen which stretched away westward from his hillside, whether his eye noted the great snow-fields on the hills bordering the distant west coast, and whether he marked the thunderstorm gathering above the Spey valley. Did his eye see, on these fine sunny days, the stags moving up out of the big glen beneath and making their way up his corrie, cropping the green grass which carpeted the ground near the wells, and during the heat of the day seeking the dwindling snow-beds, to lie lazily on their cool surface till the sun was dipping towards the hills in the far nor'-west ? Maybe he saw it all, I think ; and yet, this being his home, he took the fine sights as a matter of course, for I am sure that the Snow Bunting is a philosophical bird.

To the Highlanders the Snow Bunting was held as a sacred thing, along with the Robin, the Wren, and the Crossbill. A curious tradition is related of this bird. A hillman went to a certain holy well to draw water. He found a fire burning there with a brazen pot hanging over it. The fire was made of dried horse-dung, and the pot was filled with Snow Buntings. Around the fire were seated a number of tacharans—the spirits of unbaptized children—clothed with white. The Highlander requested that the pot should be given him. His request was re-fused. It was repeated thrice, with certain forms, and then the man was allowed to take it, but with a curse attached to it that " Nach seasadh an coinneamh Shraspe ach aon bhonaid, gu ruidh tre àl dheth na thigeadh na dheigh " (There would not stand in the gathering of Strathspey but one bonnet for three generations of those who should come after him.) I believe that this curse is held to have been fulfilled.

Although for many years the Snow Bunting was supposed to rear her young on the highest Scottish hills, the first authenticated nest was not found till 1886, and I doubt whether since that day a dozen nests have been seen throughout the whole of Scotland. As far back as 1830 MacGillivray puts it on record that he saw a male Snow Bunting on a certain snowfield on Ben Mac Dhui, and the record is of interest because of the fact that I have seen the birds on this very field nearly a century after. Writing at a still earlier date, Buffon narrates that " It is observable that the Snow Buntings sleep little or none in the night, and begin to hop by the earliest dawn. Perhaps this is the reason why they prefer the lofty mountains of the north in summer, where the day lasts the whole season." It is certainly the case that the Snow Bunting is, without exception, the earliest bird to commence to salute the coming day, though it does not continue its song, I think, to late dusk as do the Mavis and the Robin at lower and more civilised levels. In Spitzbergen, away beyond the Arctic Circle, the Snow Bird is the only songster to be heard in the land. Here the sun is above the horizon throughout the night, and I have wondered whether there is any sustained pause in the Bunting's song during the hours when darkness would prevail in countries lying beyond the rays of the midnight sun.

The flight of the Snow Bird is usually heavy in comparison with that of the other mountain nesting-birds— the Twite, the Meadow Pipit, and the Wheatear—and to a certain extent resembles that of the Corn Bunting. The curious hesitating or wildly erratic flights of the male during the nesting season are, I think, quite peculiar to it.

It is doubtful whether those birds nesting on the high Scottish hills remain in the glens of their nesting country throughout the winter; but towards October flocks of Snow Buntings appear from the lands lying to our north, and frequent the high tops, till snow drives them to shelter. In the glens they feed actively on the seeds of the hill grasses, but they are restless and are difficult to approach, uttering twittering cries, and, sometimes, their clear whistling call, as they take wing and make their way to new grounds. But it is not easy to realise that these birds are of the same species as those which reared their young in the high corries, for, curiously enough, the cock Snow Bunting has more white on his plumage during the summer months, and on the approach of autumn exchanges many of his snowy feathers for those bearing a russet tint. Even when the birds are flocked it is doubtful whether unions formed during the nesting season are dissolved, for I have seen, in the dead of winter, a Snow Bunting feed his mate as they perched with others from the flock on a stack of oats. It is perhaps during the month of March that the Snow Bunting harmonises most closely with his surroundings. During that month the hills are still deep in their snowy cloak, yet the Snow Birds, the males handsome in their full breeding plumage, have already penetrated to their wild and exposed nesting sites, and the cock birds resemble closely the snowy wastes over which they flit.

One sees many Snow Buntings along the eastern coast of Scotland during the late autumn and winter months. Occasionally a male is noted still in his nesting plumage, and such an individual is at once a marked object, however large may be the flock of which he is a member. During severe weather flocks of Snow Buntings may be seen passing south along the Aberdeenshire coast.

R

After such severe weather these flocks lose their nervousness and become sufficiently confiding to enter the farmyards and to share the hens' food.

At the approach of spring they make their way northward, but at times their places may be taken by birds which have wintered farther south.

The Snow Bunting is even more than the Brambling a circumpolar bird. It is numerous in Iceland during the nesting season, and also in Spitzbergen and Novaya Zemlya. In the high north it does not go to the mountains to nest, for the cold, or rather the arctic conditions which are necessary to it, are to be found at sea-level, and its nest at times is just above the reach of the tide. A most strange nesting site, and one from which omens might well be drawn by the superstitious, was the bosom of a dead Esquimo child. In the far north, too, the Great Pied Mountain Finch, to give it its earliest name, is said to perch on trees.

The southward range of the Snow Bunting is not so extensive as that of the majority of migrants. Even in England it is by no means common. In the south of France it is found only during very severe winters, and has also been chronicled from the Azores and Africa. Many of the birds nesting within the arctic circle in Russia migrate south over that vast country, halting only in the Crimea.

Description.—During the nesting season the cock in his handsome dress is clad entirely in white with the exception of the mantle, shoulder, tail, and the last two-thirds of the primary feathers, which are black. His bill, legs, and feet are black also.

The female at this time is of a subdued brown, marked with darker brown and black, with the exception of the secondaries, which are white.

In winter plumage the male has the centre of the

forehead and crown dark rusty brown, bordered with light grey on either side. The nape is dirty white, marked with yellowish brown. Back and scapulars black, broadly margined with dull, reddish brown. Primaries black, edged with dirty white. Secondaries and wing coverts white.

A broad band of chestnut passes across the chest. Under parts white.

While the feet remain black throughout the year, the colour of the bill changes to a dark yellow on the approach of winter.

THE DIPPER OR WATER OUZEL

CINCLUS BRITANNICUS

GOBHA-DUBH, GOBHA-UISGE, FEANNAG-UISGE (*Gaelic*). Local
names:—WATER CROW, WATER PIET, KINGFISHER.

FAR up the hill burns which run concealed, maybe, till
after midsummer's day, beneath the snow tunnels they
have fashioned for themselves during the winter months,
the Water Ouzel makes its home.

But it is not along the hill burns alone that the Dipper
is to be found. Every Highland river—the Spey, the Dee,
the Tay, to name only a few at random—harbours many
Water Ouzels, but when the flat lowland country is reached
one may look in vain for this cheery water spirit, which
seems to spend quite the half of its life in the depths of
these dark pools and swift flowing shallows which make
up our Scottish waters.

One should owe a debt of thankfulness to the Dipper
if only for the fact that he is one of the few, the very few,
of our birds to utter his song during the dead of winter,
and how melodious his song is those who have listened
to it can testify, though one comes across many to whom
it is a thing unknown. When the burns are held by the
frost, and when the rivers are well-nigh choked by float-
ing ice, the Dippers migrate seawards, and one sees many
congregated near the estuaries of the larger streams, where
they are actively engaged in searching for food in water
itself almost touching the freezing-point. But in early
spring, at the first slackening of the frost, the Water
Ouzels betake themselves to their upland nesting haunts,

for they are among the first of the hill birds to make their nests. In March I have watched a pair of Dippers carrying green moss to their dome-shaped nest, but this was in a sheltered situation, and some of those birds, having their home among the high hills, do not commence to brood till the beginning of May.

During the early days of June, when big fields of snow still lingered in the great corries above, I saw a Water Ouzel with its bill full of food flying quickly up a hill burn, to where it rushed down the steep hillsides in a series of waterfalls, brilliantly white in the strong rays of the sun. With a little difficulty I found the nest. For a Dipper's it was remarkably small, and was built on a narrow ledge of rock drenched with spray from the fall above. The nest contained a brood of half-grown young, which allowed the parent birds little leisure time to themselves. The nesting site was situated about 2000 feet above sea-level, and away down in the big glen beneath lay a deep loch, the source of a broad hill stream. It was here that the Dippers obtained most of the food for their young, making many excursions up the steep rise of a couple of hundred feet which lay between the loch and the nesting site.

There are few objects which harmonise more closely with their surroundings than the nest of the Water Ouzel. Indeed, even after the exact spot has been pointed out there is sometimes difficulty in realising that the large, rounded growth of moss is indeed the home of a family of young birds. Sometimes the nest is placed only a foot or so above the usual water level, and then disaster overtakes it should a day's rain bring down the burn in spate, but these catastrophes occur in reality less frequently than might be supposed. Nesting sites of the Dipper are various. Often the nest is made in some rock behind a waterfall, where the birds have actually to fly through the water in

order to reach their young. Sometimes a stone in mid-
stream is the site chosen, and occasionally the branch of a
tree. A curious occurrence came to my notice recently. A
fisherman discovered a Dipper's nest built on a stone and,
imagining it to be merely a lump of moss, picked it up. On
discovering his mistake he set the nest down again, but
not quite in its original situation, and when I saw it the
birds were still in possession, though it seemed that a
strong wind might well blow it into the bed of the burn,
as it was now entirely without foundation.

The eggs of the Water Ouzel are pure white in colour.
From four to six is the usual number found in a clutch.
The parent bird doing duty on the nest is a close sitter,
and when disturbed flies rapidly away, uttering its alarm
cry. After a fortnight of brooding the young are hatched,
and another three weeks or so of unstinted feeding sees
them able to leave the nest. If they are disturbed before
they are ready to fly they will at times drop into the water,
for they are able to dive and swim while as yet lacking the
power of flight.

When very young they are remarkable in that they
have the fleshy gape on the sides of the mouth dilated to
an extent not observable in other birds ; the inside of the
mouth, too, is very beautifully coloured.

The Water Ouzel is said to pair for life. Two broods
are sometimes reared in the course of a season and possibly
even three at times. I doubt, however, whether the
second brood is a regular occurrence in the Highlands.
Some years ago I came across a nest of the Dipper on
which a Spotted Fly Catcher had built her nest. As
far as could be seen—it was late in the season when I
found the double nest—both birds had hatched off their
broods safely, but the Fly Catcher had left behind an
infertile egg which served to identify her nest. There is a
certain hill burn, which I know well, where the Water

Ouzel is to be seen constantly at an elevation of over 3500 feet above sea-level. I am doubtful whether the birds nest at this great altitude; they probably rear their young in a waterfall 500 feet below, but even here they are beyond the range of the Red Grouse and have the Ptarmigan as their companions. They evidently find good feeding on the higher ground. Here the burn is a succession of sandy pools—an ideal spawning ground of salmon or trout one would say, yet fish are unknown, for the falls below offer an insurmountable barrier, and thus the food of the Dippers must consist of aquatic insects.

Amongst anglers in general the Water Ouzel is blamed for much damage done by it to the ova of trout and salmon, but such blame cannot, I think, be justified from the facts. Some time ago five Dippers were killed on a certain river at a season when the trout and salmon had just spawned, in order to discover whether the birds had been feeding on the ova of those fish. These investigations were entirely favourable to the Water Ouzels. In no instance were ova found in the birds, only water beetles and aquatic larvæ. Still to those who look only superficially, the mere fact that the Water Ouzel is so often to be seen swimming and diving near the spawning beds of salmon is sufficient to condemn the " Water Crow."

Though the Dipper is so absolutely at home on the water it never dives in the true sense of the word. It flies out into the middle of a burn or river and then plunges in like a Guillemot, slightly opening its wings as it does so. Under water it is able to move rapidly, using its wings to propel itself to the different parts of the pool it may visit in quest of food. However protracted its stay under water, its plumage remains dry and silky, and is apparently impervious to wet, though this is not the case with the newly flown young.

The bird is lighter than water, and so it is not easy to

explain by what means it succeeds in holding itself at the bottom of the pool. It has been asserted that it clings to the pebbles with its feet, or that it holds itself down with rapid movements of its wings. Certainly the claws of a young Dipper are remarkably sharp, as I can testify from having handled a bird which had just left its nest for the first time. I have watched a Water Ouzel as it walked from the bank into a hill burn, and I must say that under water it appeared to move along the bottom with equal proficiency to that displayed by it on the bank. The Dipper seems to be unaffected by the most intense cold, and when the temperature is many degrees below the freezing-point may be seen disporting itself in mid-stream, taking short flights over the surface of the pool, and then alighting and splashing the water in every direction.

The Water Ouzel occupies an interesting place amongst British birds in that it is the sole representative of its family in these Islands. The Cinclididæ, the tribe to which it belongs, are an American family, resembling the Thrushes superficially in their structure. The flight of the Dipper is strong and swift, to be compared to that of the Starling, though I doubt whether it could be sustained over long distances without effort. When alarmed both birds give utterance to a sharp note of alarm, sounding like " tzeet, tzeet," and bob up and down on the stone where they happen to be standing. The Water Ouzel is a bird of peace, and it is rare for it to pursue other birds venturing near its nesting site. The only instance in which I saw a Dipper take the offensive was when it chased a Sandpiper—newly arrived from the south—from the vicinity of its nest.

On one occasion I had a Dipper's home under observation for an hour, and during this time the nest was visited only six times by the parent birds with food. On their visits to the nest I noticed that the Water Ouzels clung to its edge for only a fraction of a second and inserted their supply of food into the mouth which happened to be thrust farthest out of the nest. On June 29th I again visited the nest of the *Gobha-dubh*. As I looked into it one of the birds which was waiting expectantly near the entrance to be fed flew out, and attempted to swim against the strong current, propelling itself strongly forward with its wings. It was, indeed, remarkably at home in the water and dived repeatedly, sometimes swimming three-quarters submerged in order to escape my notice. I succeeded in capturing it, and, after a considerable amount of persuasion, was able to secure one or two photographs.

Once it succeeded in eluding me and flew out into the main stream. Just below where it lighted there was a heavy rush of water, and into this the unfortunate small bird was dragged. It disappeared in the foam of the rapid, and for some time I watched in vain for it to emerge on the surface of the pool below. At length, however, I saw it on the bank, somewhat bedraggled, but full of life, flirting its small tail and giving that curious jerking action so distinctive to the Water Crow. For a time it stood there, then waded out into the pool, where it remained standing just within its depth, seemingly unwilling to risk another fight with the waters. A moss-grown rock at the water's edge suggested the possibility of concealment, and under this the small Dipper crept, to wait the passing of danger and the reappearance of its mother.

The Dipper takes rather a longer period than most birds of its size to bring its brood to a state of maturity, and I have known of the young being still in the nest six weeks after the eggs were laid. After the nesting season the birds extend their range somewhat, but can never be said to be migratory in the true sense of the word.

It is not only amongst the mountainous districts of our Islands that the Water Ouzel has its home. In Scandinavia it is numerous, and I have seen it on the hill streams of the Maritime Alps and of the Pyrenees. It is found in Corsica and Sardinia, and extends to North-West Africa and Asia.

Description.—Upper part of head and hind neck uniform sooty brown colour, the rest of the upper parts dark grey mixed with black. The major wing coverts are black with blue grey margins. Underneath, from the bill to the breast, the Dipper is pure white, and beyond this is a patch of chestnut which extends backwards to the forepart of the abdomen. Flanks dark grey, abdomen black. Under tail coverts dark grey, tipped with brown.

In the mature young the under parts are cream coloured, the feathers being margined with grey. Upper parts greenish grey marked with black. The colouring of the adult is assumed with the second moult.

THE CRESTED TITMOUSE

PARUS CRISTATUS SCOTICUS

Mésange huppée (*French*); Haubenmeise (*German*);
Cincia col ciuffo (*Italian*).

A SMALL person indeed, and but little known even amongst
those who penetrate to his nesting site, is the Crested Titmouse. He is one of the few, the very few, birds that are
found only in one or two favoured situations in the Highlands of Scotland, and yet in these situations are fairly
plentiful in their numbers. I believe that the Crested Tit
is unknown in any county of Great Britain south of Inverness-shire, and even in that county the ornithologist may
look long and carefully without seeing a single representative of the species. For this little bird buries himself
amongst the pine woods where, for his companions, he
has the stag and the blackcock. Artificially created woodlands are not to his liking, for here he searches in vain for
those tree stumps, half hollow and crumbling with age,
where he makes his nest. And so it comes about that the
Crested Tit is found only in the ancient forests of Scots
pine, which are the relics of the great Caledonian forest
extending in former times from Fort William on the west
to Aberdeenshire on the east.

It would obviously be ill-advised to give publicity to
the chief nesting haunt of the species, though I am afraid
the district, as it is, abounds with collectors. Still I may
put it on record as an interesting fact that in the forests
of Mar and Ballochbuie, where one would expect to see
something of the birds, they are entirely absent. As a

matter of fact I doubt whether the total length of the nesting ground of the Crested Tit exceeds fifteen miles, while in width it is only four or five miles. To other parts of Scotland he is a rare or accidental visitor only. On the Continent the Crested Titmouse is widely distributed, but it is of a slightly different variety to our British representative.

I made my first acquaintance with the Crested Titmouse on a certain day early in May. After twenty-four hours of heavy rain the wind had veered round to the north and an extraordinarily severe snowstorm for the time of year had swept over the hills.

To reach the district where the Crested Tits were nesting it was necessary for me to cross a watershed where the road reached the 2000 feet level. Leaving the valley of the Dee with a northerly wind and heavy showers of rain I found that at the head of the Don conditions resembling those of mid-winter prevailed. The wind now brought with it blinding snow squalls, and the hills were heavily coated. At Cockbridge the road mounts rapidly up the hill face, and here the snow was lying to a depth of from three or four feet, the storm experienced having been actually the heaviest of the whole winter. Under the circumstances further progress was impossible, and a detour of at least seventy miles was necessary. Even then snow lay on the road, though not in quantities sufficient to retard the progress of the car. It was towards afternoon that we approached the country of the Crested Titmouse. Away before us there stretched the range of the great Cairngorm hills, heavily mantled in white. Over their slopes the wind, which had now backed to the west, was blowing with great force, sweeping up before it the powdery snow and hurrying it along in dense clouds that rose many feet from the ground and rendered the summits of the hills blurred and indistinct. The scene resembled more a cold January afternoon than a day in the "merry month."

In the big pine forest there was shelter from the wind and the air was almost mild. Deer crossed the road before us—to be rapidly lost to view among the trees—and Grey Hens rose noiselessly from the heather. For some distance we walked through the pines, and then the stalker, who was leading, pointed out to us a little clump of trees rather younger than the surrounding woodland, where the Crested Titmouse had her nest. The nesting site, we found, was at the stump of a tree long since dead, and the nest was placed in a hollow not more than three feet from the ground. The eggs were three in number, and the nest was skilfully made of moss, rabbit down, and deer's hair. It was interesting, too, to note that the moss was of a different species to that which grew on the ground beneath the tree. The bird, unfortunately, had deserted, so a search was commenced for a second nest. This was discovered before long in a dead pine standing more or less by itself amongst long heather, and the nest was placed almost at ground level in a hollow in the trunk. The mother Titmouse sat very closely and allowed herself to be inspected as she brooded on her eggs. It was indeed with some difficulty that she could be induced to leave the nest, and, when she did so, she flew only a few yards into some small trees and flitted restlessly from branch to branch, though, curiously enough, she uttered no alarm cry.

A third nest, discovered a little later on, was in a hollow about a foot from the ground, and so dark was the hole that matches had to be lit in order to discover the contents of the nest.

It was with some interest that we found that, in this instance, the mother bird had already hatched her eggs, the nest containing a number of very young babies who

had sense only to open their large mouths in a blind appeal
for food. Now it was that we heard for the first time the
alarm note of the Crested Titmouse. The main point that
strikes one, I think, is the softness of these calls compared
with the cries of the other members of the Tit family. The
notes are a low musical twittering, reminding me of a part
of the song uttered by a certain canary of my acquaintance;
they lack entirely the harshness of the cries of the Blue
or Great Tits. I have mentioned that, in order to see into
this nest, a match was lighted and held in the hollow. No
more was thought of the incident at the time, but a fortnight later the stalker and I revisited the spot to see what
progress the young had made. A charred and blackened
stump was all that remained of the former nesting site !
In a way that it is impossible to account for the match had
set alight the crumbling wood, and thus a most pathetic
and greatly to be regretted tragedy had been enacted
in the quiet forest. Of the young there was no trace ;
the nest was burnt almost to a cinder, and their small
corpses had been effectually cremated.

On May 28th I revisited the one nest where things had
gone well with the owners, and found that the family had
just been hatched out. The tree was well placed for
photographing the parent birds near the nest, and as
they appeared to be quite confiding I focussed a certain
branch of the tree where they were in the habit of
alighting and waited for events. At the moment when
I erected the camera both the parent birds were away
searching for food, and when they returned to find the
formidable apparatus fixed up in front of their house
they were extremely surprised. The cock was much the
bolder of the two. He perched fearlessly on the nesting
tree, and scolded the camera and the photographer continuously until he became wearied and his voice went.
In the meanwhile the hen flitted anxiously around, hold-

ing in her mouth a succulent caterpillar which she ham-
mered repeatedly on a branch whenever it showed signs
of protest. She very rarely uttered her alarm cry.
From time to time both birds flew off together as though
to discuss the next move, but soon returned with undu-
lating flight. After standing for a time on the dead tree
in which his nest was situated, the cock often moved off
to a small fir near, balancing himself, with legs planted
wide apart, on the topmost branches or searching actively
for the small " aphis " on which the birds seemed to feed
very largely. Sometimes the bird summoned up sufficient courage to drop down and cling on to the edge of
the hollow in which his young were waiting expectantly
to be fed, but he would not actually enter the hole while
I was there.

When I moved off a little way, however, both birds
entered the nest fearlessly, taking small notice of the
camera. On one occasion they seemed to be accompanied
by a Coal Tit, the latter probably having been attracted
to the scene by their anxious cries. It was only occasionally that the cock appeared with food while I was at the
tree, and then he soon got tired of holding the grub in
his beak and made a meal of it, cleaning his bill carefully
on a branch after his repast. I noted that when the hen
returned from a foraging expedition and found that I had
taken up my position near the tree, she at once flew off
to search for her mate, evidently relying upon him for
support and for guidance.

If I remained for long at the nest the birds, especially
the female, drooped and quivered their wings, from anxiety,
I think. In appearance the two birds closely resembled
each other. Each had the same prominent crest, which
appeared to be raised or depressed at will. Each, too,
had the same black collar and tie and the same grey head.
It was only occasionally that the male Titmouse uttered

the two high notes which the Coal and Great Tits make use of continually at the beginning of their alarm call.

A pair of Redstarts had their nest near to the hollow tree, and sometimes appeared to watch the scene with anxiety. Life there was in plenty in the forest. From a tree near the clear wild song of a Missel Thrush was thrown out over the wood. Nearer at hand a shy Willow Warbler—that bird of most graceful and delicate appearance—was singing to himself in melodious, warbling notes as he fluttered among the pine needles in his quest for insects. At times the less melodious, yet interesting, song of the Tree Pipit came from one of the higher firs, the bird often leaving his perch to flutter up into the air and soar earthward in characteristic flight. At times also Black-headed Gulls crossed overhead, uttering their sharp call notes, and a Goosander flew rapidly northward, following the course of the burn. Near by was a very old dead stump fifteen feet or so in height, where a pair of crested titmice had their nest for several years in succession ; but though the working of the birds was visible on the trunk, the nesting site was unoccupied. It should be mentioned that, unlike the Blue or Great Tits, the Crested Titmouse often fashions a hole for itself in a decayed tree. It is thus of considerable importance to the small worker that the wood should be in the right condition. A tree which is crumbling is discarded after a test of its suitability has been made, also one which is too hard for the small bill to drive its way into. One often comes across such commencements of nesting sites in the forest ; sometimes the tree has been abandoned after considerable impression has been made on the wood.

It is during April that the new nesting hollows are formed or former ones refurnished, and the eggs are laid during the first week of May. A stalker told me that on one occasion he noticed that the hen Titmouse laid two or three eggs, then disappeared entirely from the nesting site, and returned more than a week later to complete her clutch. Although several degrees of frost had been experienced in the interval, every egg was hatched successfully. The fact is of interest, for I have known precisely the same thing occur in the case of the Long-tailed Tit. The eggs of the Crested Titmouse generally number from four to seven. In shape and in colour they closely resemble those of the Blue Tit, but are, I think, a trifle larger in size. On a white ground colour spots of a red brown are implanted, the spots being more numerous at the large end of the egg. In size they measure about ·63 by ·49 of an inch.

In addition to their alarm note, uttered when nesting, the Crested Tits throughout the year call to each other in a shrill piercing whistle. This whistle is pitched, I think, in a higher key than the same note of the Coal Tit, but has a lesser volume of sound.

Although the food of the Crested Tit consists mainly of insects in their mature or larval forms, it is fond of fat, resembling the Coal Tit in this taste. When a hind is shot in the forest, and is for some reason or other left out for a few hours after being " gralloched," the Crested Tits from the neighbourhood congregate rapidly and feed greedily on the fat surrounding the animal's kidneys, picking them clean in a short space of time. Also when deerskins are hung up outside the larder the Tits may be seen actively searching for pieces of fat.

In spite of the frequent excursions into its country of egg-collectors and gunners—I am told that a representative of the British Museum shot a number of the birds in a certain forest recently—the Crested Titmouse appears to be holding its own in its remote strongholds. Its hardiness is great, and it never, even during the most severe winter weather, leaves its native forests, where it

s

is within sight of the great hills which harbour in their corries fields of eternal snow.

On June 9th I visited the family of the Crested Tits for the last time. For some days wild weather had been experienced in the glen, and on the high hills snow had been driven fast before a biting nor'-easter. On peering into the nesting hollow I saw that the youngsters were full fledged—to my knowledge they were fourteen days old—and one, standing on his fellows, seemed to be debating a sortie into the outer world. Soon the hen bird appeared, with her mouth crammed full of food for the small people who were expectantly awaiting her arrival, and now I looked for the coming of the cock—the small and courageous husband who used to stand on the tree a few feet from me and curse me roundly for daring to disturb the peace of his home. But of him there was no sign. At times, indeed, the hen went off for a few moments as though to find him and to seek his support, but she returned alone after each search. Suddenly her soft scolding notes ceased abruptly, and looking skywards I saw a Kestrel soaring in circles at a great height. His keen eye was searching the wood, and he appeared to be quite heedless of my presence. More than likely he had, on a previous visit, snatched away the small father of the family. It seemed to me as I watched that there was a certain pathetic air of expectancy about the survivor. She seemed to be waiting for her mate, and to be at a loss to know what had happened to him—a tragedy which might touch many a heart. And yet in Nature such tragedies are of daily, hourly occurrence.

To us, possessing as we do a consciousness and a memory retentive of sorrow, it almost appears that Nature is without compassion, merciless. And yet if we ponder the matter it will appear to us in a different light. Though Death is everywhere showing his hand in the universe, and life preys upon life, yet one finds there no sorrows save those which are fleeting ones. The joy of life is over all living things. Half an hour after the narrowest of escapes from the Eagle the Grouse will be crowing loudly and cheerily ; half an hour after being pursued by the Sparrow Hawk the Song Thrush will be singing happily. And only with consciousness and a striving to understand the why and the wherefore does pain come.

With the passing of the Kestrel the Crested Titmouse recommenced her scolding, and with such effect that she soon gathered round her sympathetic neighbours. A passing Coal Tit could scarcely have shown more anxiety even if its own young had been in danger, and a Chaffinch called excitedly. As the mother Titmouse refused to come near the nest while I was standing by, I took what shelter a neighbouring juniper bush afforded, and watched her from there. After a time she gathered courage sufficient to light on the dead branch the cock had used as a perch, and then at least half a dozen times flew down and held on to the edge of the hollow before she could bring herself to enter with the food she carried in her bill. For a moment she was out of sight, attending to the sanitary arrangements in the nest, then she emerged and flew off in quest of more food. As it was impossible to obtain satisfactory photographs of the young in the nest, I removed the least active and set him upon a branch. It was not an easy matter to induce him to hold on to the wood with his small feet—he much preferred my own fingers—but after a certain amount of patience I succeeded in getting one or two photographs of him.

A second member of the family I removed for the same purpose was more fully developed, and determinedly refused to sit for his photograph, calling loudly and shrilly, and, immediately he had an opportunity, flying off strongly to a neighbouring pine. The moment he started his flight the mother bird flew up and escorted her child, encouraging him as she did so. I removed a third youngster, but with no better results ; and now the two remaining members of the family emerged from their nest of their own accord and took short, feeble flights, barely rising above the surface of the heather. At first they were unable to rise sufficiently to settle on the pine branches, but it was instructive to notice how with every flight their wing-power strengthened, until it was not always easy to distinguish them from the parent bird, who escorted them on each of their excursions. Even after the last of her brood had left the nest she did not seem altogether to realise that this was the case, and several times alighted on the dead tree, looking down towards the empty nest with her bill full of food. In the young birds the crest was showing, though it was not so prominent as that of their mother, and their black collars were also noticeable. I examined the nest, and found that it was built almost entirely of deer's hair and rabbit down, the moss, if any had originally been present, having dried up and being invisible as one looked down from above.

The sun shone warmly among the pines as I took my leave of the Crested Tit family, and I left them with the hope that things would prosper with them, and that the marauding Kestrel would not pass again that way.

Description.—The male and female Crested Titmouse differ only slightly from each other, and there is no seasonal change of coloration.

Length, 4·5 inches. In the middle the crown feathers are elongated and tipped with white, forming the conspicuous crest which can to a certain extent be lowered or raised at will. The forehead, the sides of the head, and neck are white. A black line runs backwards from the eye and downwards, partly encircling the ear coverts. A second black band runs from the nape downward, and

YOUNG, CRESTED TITMOUSE.

A BABY CRESTED TIT AFTER ITS FIRST FLIGHT.

terminates in a well-marked black gorget covering the foreneck and throat. Upper parts grey brown. Wings and tail marked by grey. Inner secondaries have pale tips. Breast and abdomen white, flanks and under tail coverts buff. Legs and toes lead-coloured. The female has the crest not quite so conspicuous, but otherwise closely resembles the male. In young birds the crest is smaller and the upper parts darker and greyer. Cheeks white with buff tinge, under parts duller.

THE SANDPIPER

TRINGA HYPOLEUCA

Luatharan, Luatharan-glas, Cama-lúbach (*Gaelic*); Chevalier guig-nette (*French*); Fluss-ufer läufer (*German*). Local names :— White-breasted Weet-weet, Willy Wicket, Water Junket, Fiddler, Summer Snipe.

One of the most pleasing sounds which herald the advance of spring is the tuneful, whistling call of the Sandpiper. It is mid-April before these birds of passage arrive on our coasts, and almost immediately make their way up the rivers and hill-burns where they have their nesting sites.

They find a smiling country awaiting them. On the river-banks birches are putting forth their foliage of that tender green which they retain till Midsummer's Day is past. The Oyster-Catchers are already at their summer homes, and are occupied with the commencement of household duties when the Sandpipers arrive. The Goosanders are brooding in their dark nesting hollows, and the young of the Mallard have by now seen the day. Like the Oyster-Catchers, the Sandpipers make the journey up the rivers in easy stages. They are already paired when they arrive at that particular part of the stream where last season they successfully reared their brood. One such site I know well. To the north the ground slopes up abruptly, shutting out the cold, snow-laden winds off the high hills from the dwelling-place of the Summer Snipe. When the Sandpipers reach their destination the river is running full with the melting of the snows.

One can always distinguish this snow-water or " snaa

bree " : it is rarely peat-coloured or muddy, but is wonderfully clear even when the river is in spate. Before the
Sandpipers came no sound was heard on the river here
save the whistle of a passing Oyster-Catcher or the call
of a Golden Plover, but now there is music everywhere,
for not one pair only, but numbers of Sandpipers, flit
backward and forward over the rushing water. They
move, it seems, only the fraction of an inch above the
stream with a flight that is grace personified. They cannot
thrust their wings downward in order to obtain their
driving force—if they did so they would be immersed in
the water—so they hold them V-shape above the head,
and the wing-beat is only half completed. This V-shape
formation is especially apparent just before the birds
alight on some rounded stone projecting above the
water's surface. One April day I went down to the
nesting site of the Sandpipers after a time of rain and
wintry weather. The morning sun fell on the birches,
turning their half-formed leaves the colour of silver, and
the trees gave unstintedly of their aroma, so that the air
was heavy and perfume-laden. The sky this morning
was of an extraordinary clearness, and every snowfield
on the higher hills was distinct. The Sandpipers were
demonstrative, and constantly crossed and recrossed the
river, toying and playing with each other. When they
alighted, they repeatedly wagged their tails up and down
in the manner so characteristic to them ; but they were
restless, and it was not long before they again started out,
full of the joy of life and of springtide. Gradually black
clouds spread across the sky, and soon a tropical downpour of rain and hail ruffled the surface of the water.
The Sandpipers, their ardour considerably damped, stood
about disconsolately, while a Stock Dove, which I had
disturbed from brooding her two callow young in a rabbit
burrow at the top of a sandbank, flew anxiously round,

eager to return to her young. Soon the storm passed, and the sun once more shone out and the air was clear. To the west the hills appeared again, but within the space of an hour they had been clad in a white coating of hail, the strips of recently-burnt heather standing out conspicuously by reason of their greater whiteness.

On every mountain loch up to 2000 feet above sea-level the Sandpiper is found. One such loch sees many pairs with the return of each nesting season. A road winds its way up the glen to a solitary shooting lodge, and twice daily a motor car, bearing the mails to and from the post-office, thirteen miles distant, passes along it.

One season, towards the end of May, a Sandpiper made her nest within a few yards of the road. Although her eggs were laid amongst long heather, where she was hidden from sight so long as she sat closely, the Summer Snipe never mastered the suspicions which took posses-sion of her at the approach of the car. Invariably she left her nest, and, moving to a little clearing a few feet away, stood expectantly on the watch, a charming and conspicuous object. If the car was driven past her with no slackening of speed she remained standing there, but if the driver slowed down she at once rose and flew down to the loch-side in silence. Even after she had been brooding close on three weeks, and her eggs were on the point of hatching, she showed the same restlessness, but notwithstanding the number of occasions on which she was disturbed, she hatched off her brood safely.

In contrast to her behaviour was the attitude adopted by a second Sandpiper nesting above the loch on a burn-side. On the occasion when I was shown her nest she remained on her eggs even when I watched her at the distance of only a few feet ; she crouched low on the ground, and evidently trusted to her harmonisation with her surroundings. This particular bird hatched out her

brood one cloudless morning of June when the burn
beside her nest was running low and clear, and at once
became the most anxious, agitated mother when I approached the spot where the chicks were lying concealed.
Both she and the cock bird hovered near with shrill whistlings, endeavouring to decoy me from the neighbourhood,
and arousing alarm amongst all the bird world in the
neighbourhood.

One rarely finds Sandpipers' eggs before the middle
of May, nor after the third week in June, for the birds
are regular in their nesting. There is reason to suppose
that they pair for life, for every spring they return to the
same part of a river or glen. In one instance a Sandpiper
was found nesting in exactly the same spot for seven
years. When disturbed the hen Sandpiper usually runs
for some little distance from her nest before taking wing,
and, if she has been brooding for some time, gives utterance to a long-drawn plaintive whistle, uttered in a very
high key, as she stands on some stone watching anxiously
the intruder at her nesting site.

The exact vertical range of the Sandpiper in the Highlands is doubtful. On the lochs of the Cairngorm hills
it is absent, though there are several such lochs situated
at, or just over, the 3000 feet line, where one might expect
to meet with it. On the Dee it is found nesting as far as
the lower end of the Garbhchoire, a little over 2000 feet.
Mr. Harvie Brown places it on record that he has in two
successive seasons noticed a pair on Ben Chaorin, 2700 feet
above the level of the sea, and I have sometimes seen the
birds only a few hundred feet lower. Unlike the Dunlin, it
does not care for peaty lochans, but prefers clear lochs with
dry ground surrounding them, or rushing hill-burns, for,
in contrast to the Dunlin, its food consists almost entirely
of insects. On still days of June, and more especially
towards the evening, one sees many Sandpipers moving

across the surface of some hill loch where they are nesting, and picking up many insects on the wing. Throughout the night they may be heard uttering their cries, for, like the Oyster Catchers, they appear to be active during the whole of the twenty-four hours, snatching a few minutes of sleep at odd intervals throughout that time.

The nest of the Sandpiper is rudimentary, but I think that a deeper hollow is scraped than is the case with the majority of the waders. The eggs always number four. Their ground colour is a pale red brown, and they have underlying shell markings of pinkish tinge as well as darker blotches and spots. They are pear-shaped, and lie in the nest with the small ends towards the centre. The period of incubation is about three weeks, and the young are able to move actively about from the first. They sometimes take to the water and swim fairly well. They are covered with down of a brownish grey colour above, with a brownish black band down the back. The lower parts are white.

Towards the end of July the young Sandpipers become full-fledged, and almost at once young and old make their way down the burns to the rivers, and so to the coast, from where the southern migration is commenced.

In the Hebrides the Sandpiper is common ; here it is known as the Little Fiddler, on account of its habit of vibrating its body and its piping notes. It nests, too, in the Orkneys and Shetlands.

There are few of our " waders " which have so extensive a breeding range as the Sandpiper. Northward it nests up to the North Cape. It is found on the river Petschora. South of these islands it nests amongst the mountains of Spain, Portugal, and Italy, and is also found in Turkey, Greece, and the Caucasus. It is also reported as nesting in Tunisia.

In autumn the southward migrations of the Sandpiper

extends to Cape Colony, and throughout Southern Asia to Ceylon and the Malay Peninsula. It is found also in Australia and Tasmania, though it is doubtful if the birds nesting in this country reach these far-distant lands.

Description.—Upper parts brown, striated on crown and neck, and with arrow-shaped markings of umber on the back. Wing coverts and inner secondaries barred, major coverts and secondaries tipped, with white, bases of inner webs of inner primaries white, forming a continuous white bar in the extended wing. The lower back, rump, upper tail coverts, and tail of a bronze green colour. The tail barred with umber and tipped with white. Under parts white, lined with slaty black on neck and forebreast.

When fledged the young are light greyish brown above, the feathers margined with two bands, one dusky, the other reddish. Forepart and sides of neck greyish with faint dusky lines. Rest of the plumage white. Wings and tail as in adult.

Male and female Sandpipers are alike in plumage, and there is only a slight seasonal change of coloration. Length 8¾ inches, extent of wings 14 inches. The spring and autumn moults take place at its winter quarters.

THE DUNLIN

EROLIA ALPINA

GILLE-FEADAIG, POLLARAN, TARMACHAN-TRÀGHAD (*Gaelic*); BECASSEAU VARIABLE (*French*); ALPEN TRANDLAÜFER (*German*); PESTROSOBORG PESSOTCHNIK (*Russian*). Local names:—DUNLIN SANDPIPER, SEA SNIPE, LEAST SNIPE, PURRE.

To many the Dunlin is known during the months of winter, but through the long days of the year, when the birds seek the high moorlands for the purpose of rearing their young, they merge into obscurity. Then they are seen only by the hill-shepherd, or the stalker moving round the tops in search, maybe, of a deer calf, or, again, of a fox's den. They have little experience of man and his ways, these mountain birds, and thus they show a degree of confidence which is often quite noteworthy, and possessing great charm for one whose aim is to study wild nature at close quarters.

The Dunlin which nest on our Scottish hills are of a different race to those which one sees during the months of winter haunting the estuaries of so many of our rivers. They retire south of these Islands at the approach of cold weather, and it is not until May that they reach their mountain haunts, arriving long after the Greenshank has made its appearance, and having, perhaps, the Dotterel as their companions on their northward flight.

During the month of May one sees, too, parties of Dunlin still frequenting the coast-line, though they have by now assumed their handsome wedding dress, but these small people press on northward ; they are waiting for the melting of the snows in the countries of the High North, where it is not until June that the grip of winter slackens.

The Dunlins are probably already paired when they arrive on our hills, but it is not until the first days of June that the hen birds scrape the insignificant hollows that serve as their nests, and deposit their inconspicuous eggs, four in number.

It was on such an early June day that I made an expedition into the home of the Dunlin. The air was redolent with the many sweet scents which seem to be inseparable to the season of early summer on the high grounds. The blaeberry plants yielded up their perfume ; the young shoots of heather, crowberry, and cranberry added their gift. On a high ridge a big herd of deer were standing, where they were outlined with great distinctness against the sky. Some fine heads there were in the herd, and they appeared all the more imposing by reason of the velvet which still covered their growing antlers. After a stiff climb the big plateau, stretching away for miles at a height of close on 3000 feet above sea-level, was reached. Here the Dunlin have their home, and have as their companions the Golden Plover, the high-nesting Grouse, and the white-winged Ptarmigan. But while the other birds seek the shelter of the glens in winter, or even move south beyond our confines, the Ptarmigan remains, for is he not, in the thoughts of the Highlander, *An t-Eun Adhar*, the Bird of the Frost ? Many springs have their source in the plateau of the Dunlin, and in many directions do the burns from them make their way down to the low grounds.

Along one of these burns the way led for a time, where the grass was springing quickly after its long imprisonment beneath the snow. One snow-patch still lingered ; it was not many yards in extent, and on its surface there lay the peat and other debris drifted on to it before the storms which so often sweep the plateau during the dark months. On the snow a couple of hinds were seeking

relief from the heat, although the extent of the snow was
scarcely sufficient to harbour them. At our sudden
appearance at close quarters from behind a sheltering
ridge they sprang up in alarm and fled precipitately. A
little farther on a hind by herself suggested the probability
of her having a calf concealed somewhere in the neighbourhood, but this surmise was not substantiated by a
search. At length we reached that particular part of the
plateau where the Dunlin have their haunt.

A little loch lies here. Its waters are rarely quiet;
they are exposed to the winds from every quarter of the
compass. Round the lochan peat-hags extend for a considerable distance, and the white flowers of the cotton-
grass catch the breeze.

It was near the lochan that I had my first sight of the
bird for which I searched. A male Dunlin, handsome in
his black breast, which he assumes only during the nesting
season, was probing the soft peat in a little basin. I
was almost upon him before he realised my approach,
but he showed surprisingly little concern, and merely
walked off quietly towards the small loch. For a time I
sought for his mate, searching the grass and heather in
the vicinity, and then moved down to the lochan. My
bird was standing on its shore, and this time took wing,
flying over the water as he uttered his peculiar purring
cry. I was convinced that his mate was brooding in the
neighbourhood. For a time I watched him. The heat
till now had been oppressive, but with the passing of the
noontide there rose a wind from out of the south-west,
ruffling the dark peaty waters of the lochan and dispersing
the clouds overhead. Eastward, over the Cairngorms,
dark clouds settled on the hills, and against the wind
came the rumble of far-distant thunder. To the south
of the lochan the ground rose gradually, and from this
direction the friend who accompanied me on the expedi-

tion appeared, walking rapidly. His news was that he had flushed a Dunlin, which, from her behaviour, he imagined must have a nest in the vicinity, but had been unable to find the nest. We at once made our way back to the spot, and found the Dunlin Sandpiper standing quietly a short distance away. Until we had almost reached her she stood there, then, feigning a broken leg, unless, indeed, she had in reality come by an accident, she moved a little farther off.

We remained waiting quietly for some time, then the Dunlin, flying back, alighted without sound a few yards from us. But we were evidently too near her nest to permit of her returning to it. Moving, therefore, to another part of the hill, we lay down where we had a good view of the small bird, marking her until she settled down out of sight. As we again approached her she rose and fluttered off before us. The nest, however, was remarkably difficult to discover ; indeed, it was only as we were abandoning the search that we came across it. Placed among some short grass, it was hidden away in quite a noteworthy manner, and was scarcely more conspicuous than that of a skylark. The nesting hollow was of the slightest, and in it lay three small eggs harmonising closely with their surroundings. To all appearances they had been laid only a very short time ; indeed, it is possible that the fourth egg had not as yet been deposited, and so I decided to return at a somewhat later date in the endeavour to photograph the sitting bird. A fortnight later, when the Dunlin should have been sitting close, I again visited the plateau.

The day was an unsuitable one for photography, for a cold west wind hurried over the high ground, bringing with it the breath of winter. On our way we passed the spot where a Grouse had hatched off her brood, and a little later flushed a second Grouse brooding her family

against the cold wind. As their mother fluttered away
the chicks commenced to shiver, and sought what shelter
they could, half burying their small bodies in any crevices
amongst the peat-hags. We reached the Dunlin's nesting
site, but for a time were unable to find the nest. But
then we came across a sucked egg-shell, and a little later
the primitive hollow quite deserted. In all probability
the tragedy was the work of a stoat, which had scented
out and sucked the eggs, for I think it scarcely probable
that a Gull or Hoodie could have discovered them.

We moved down to the lochan, watched, as we did so,
by more than one pair of Golden Plover which had hatched
off their brood since our last visit and were calling plain-
tively and continuously, and almost at once disturbed a
male Dunlin on guard. The bird rose into the wind, and,
after wheeling and dashing through the air, came to rest
on a knoll near, uttering characteristic scraping cries. A
little farther along we saw his mate amongst some tufty
grass ; but as we approached she disappeared mysteriously, and so we moved forward till we reached the edge
of the plateau and looked down into the deep corrie beneath, leaving the Dunlin to return to their young.

In the corrie the air was still, and many hinds with
their attendant calves could be seen crossing the burn
far beneath us. A few yards away there lay the fast-
diminishing field of snow that at times lingers in the
corrie till late in the summer. Heavy masses of black
cloud hurried past overhead, moving at great speed, and
from time to time the hills were hidden in thick rain-
squalls. After a time I moved back to the Dunlin ground,
while my companion continued on his way. Again the
cock Dunlin rose from the moss. This time, after dashing
backwards and forwards, he came above my head and
soared in the teeth of the gale for some little time.

His wings were motionless ; yet he stood his ground,

and I could not but feel how clumsy even the flight of the Snipe was compared with the finished movements of this Dunlin Sandpiper. The fashion, too, in which, after skimming the moor down wind with the speed of an express train, he wheeled abruptly about and alighted on a knoll almost instantaneously, compelled the admiration. This knoll was not more than twenty-five yards from me, and so, as the bird stood head to wind with little sign of uneasiness, I commenced to stalk him, inch by inch, obtaining a number of photographs at different ranges before his suspicions were aroused and he moved off, running, however, only a few yards before remaining as though on guard.

It was about this time that I saw the hen in precisely the same locality as before. She showed much more anxiety than the cock, uttering almost incessantly two alarm notes as she walked round me. One of these notes was the characteristic trill, unlike, I think, any other cry in the bird world ; the other, which appeared to be the note of extra alarm, was a harsh cry reminding me much of the alarm note of the Lesser Tern. In order to observe the effect, I called several times, imitating the cry of one of her chicks. The effect was striking and instantaneous ; the bird rushed up in alarm, and literally rolled herself about on the ground with feathers ruffled. She indeed presented such an appearance that it was quite impossible to see her head or feet emerging from the dishevelled bundle into which she rolled herself. Evidently her tactics were quite different—considerably less elegant, but perhaps equally forcible—to those used by the Dotterel under similar circumstances. After a time she began to realise that her deception was producing no effect on the object of her mistrust, and moved anxiously round me.

Her mate, evidently considering that his responsibilities ended with his flight signalising my arrival, be-

T

trayed little anxiety as to the welfare of his young, but occasionally, after an outburst of alarm on the part of his mate, roused himself somewhat from his apparent apathy— he stood most of the time with his feathers puffed out facing the biting wind—and moved uneasily for a short distance before again taking up his sentinel-like position. But though both birds evinced the utmost confidence in approaching me, they did not cease from warning their young to remain concealed ; and after waiting for two hours—by which time I had become just about as cold as is possible—I was obliged to leave the nesting site, since I feared that the arctic wind would have a disastrous effect on the Dunlin brood.

Across the glen there stretched a second great plateau, and here, on crossing a sheep-fence, I got close to a male Golden Plover on sentinel duty. Facing the strong wind, he had not been aware of my approach, and seemed at first too surprised to utter his alarm note. As he awoke to the sense of his responsibilities he repeatedly uttered his alarm whistle, and from the far side of the fence his mate answered him. Their excited calls aroused, in the neighbourhood of a lochan near, a Dunlin who also evidently had young, for she flew backward and forward with powerful zigzagging flight, uttering her characteristic note. From time to time she alighted at various points, holding her wings above her head with most graceful poise for a few seconds after she touched ground. Immediately I imitated the cry of her young, however, she rose from wherever she happened to be standing and flew round, betraying great disquietude. Like the young of all the waders, the Dunlin chicks crouch on the ground immediately danger is signalled by their parents, and remain in hiding till they are informed that they may show themselves ; and on this occasion also I was unsuccessful in discovering them.

Considering that the Dunlin and the Common Snipe approach each other so nearly in size—the whole length of a Snipe is about $10\frac{1}{2}$ inches, whereas that of the Dunlin is 8 inches—it is surprising how much smaller are the eggs of the latter bird.

The nesting hollow is also much more rudimentary, and I doubt whether Dunlin are partial to the boggy ground so much sought after by Snipe. They take their young after they have been hatched to such ground, it is true, but as a nesting site I am inclined to think they prefer a dry hillside with a lochan near, and make their nests in the short hill grass that affords them a certain amount of cover.

The Dunlin is essentially a northern bird in its nesting. Outside this country it breeds in the Faroes, and is also found in Iceland, though it does not, I believe, remain on that island through the winter months. It is believed to breed in Greenland. Throughout Norway it is plentiful, nesting beyond the Arctic Circle. In Russia and Lapland it is abundant, its range extending as far as Novaya Zemlya. It also nests in Denmark and in the northern districts of Germany. A very few are said to nest as far south as Spain and Italy.

During the autumn and winter months the Dunlin, in its migration, spreads far over many countries. It is found in Africa and Egypt, frequenting the course of the Nile. It extends its range to the Red Sea, India, and Japan. In Eastern Asia and Northern America it is replaced by an allied race. On Cheviot (2700 feet above sea-level), on the borders of England and Scotland, several pairs of Dunlin usually nest. I have only once—in early July—visited the wild plateau which serves as a nesting-ground, and although I saw several birds feeding by the tarns on the hill-top, they did not, from their careless behaviour, appear to possess broods. After the season of their nesting the Dunlin lose their handsome black breasts ; indeed, an observer being familiar with them only when they frequent the coast during the winter months would scarcely recognise them at their nesting sites. More than any bird the Dunlin possess the remarkable power of wheeling and doubling as one individual at an instant's notice, even when they are in great flocks, and it would be interesting to know by what means the sudden order is communicated to the assembly.

Description.—The adult male in summer plumage has the bill black and top of the head almost black. Neck greyish white streaked with black. Feathers of the back and scapulars black, with rufous edges. Wing coverts ash grey. Pimaries grey black with white shafts. Secondaries grey black edged with white. Rump and upper tail coverts black and grey. Tail grey and brown. Chin white. Breast handsomely coloured with black, a few white feathers appearing. Vent, thighs, under tail coverts white. Legs and feet black. The females are rather larger than the males, weighing 2 oz. against 1½ oz., the weight of the male. Their plumage resembles that of the cock birds.

In winter the Dunlin loses its black breast, its under parts becoming almost white, and the whole bird is less brightly coloured.

Albino Dunlins have very occasionally been recorded, but the bird is subject to a good deal of variation in its plumage.

INDEX

PRINTED IN GREAT BRITAIN BY
LOWE AND BRYDONE (PRINTERS) LTD., LONDON.